Focus on U.S. History:

The Era of the Civil War and Reconstruction

Kathy Sammis

J. WESTON

WALCH

PUBLISHER

Portland, Maine

User's Guide
to
Walch Reproducible Books

As part of our general effort to provide educational materials that are as practical and economical as possible, we have designated this publication a "reproducible book." The designation means that purchase of the book includes purchase of the right to limited reproduction of all pages on which this symbol appears:

Here is the basic Walch policy: We grant to individual purchasers of this book the right to make sufficient copies of reproducible pages for use by all students of a single teacher. This permission is limited to a single teacher and does not apply to entire schools or school systems, so institutions purchasing the book should pass the permission on to a single teacher. Copying of the book or its parts for resale is prohibited.

Any questions regarding this policy or requests to purchase further reproduction rights should be addressed to:

Permissions Editor
J. Weston Walch, Publisher
321 Valley Street • P. O. Box 658
Portland, Maine 04104-0658

1   2   3   4   5   6   7   8   9   10
ISBN 0-8251-3338-6

CONTENTS

UNIT 3. THE PERSONAL FACE OF WAR

UNIT 4. RECONSTRUCTION

CREDITS

Civil War Memorabilia CD:	pages *vii*, 38, 39, 59, 67
Corbis-Bettmann:	pages 3, 64, 78, 79
Dover Pictorial Archive:	pages 5, 14, 15, 17, 18, 19, 20, 25, 26, 30, 37, 47, 61, 65, 68, 70, 75, 86, 87, 88
Kansas State Historical Society, Topeka:	page 16
The Library of Congress	page 28
Arms, Armor, and Battles CD:	pages 31, 33, 42, 50, 51, 55, 58
Davenport Daily Gazette, Iowa:	pages 36, 43, 63
North Wind Picture Archives:	pages 49, 56, 62, 76, 77, 80, 81, 90, 91, 93

TO THE TEACHER

The Civil War was a critical and pivotal event in U.S. history. The continued existence of the United States as a single, unified nation hinged on the war's outcome, and the victory by the North finally ended slavery and greatly expanded application of the ideals set forth in the Declaration of Independence. The war was the perhaps inevitable climax of decades of sectional tensions and conflict, and the federal victory permanently dampened strong claims of states' rights. After the war, the ruined South went through a period of Reconstruction that brought about great changes in the lives of both blacks and whites but ultimately ended with whites once again suppressing their black fellow citizens. In studying this era, students will gain an understanding of the critical issues involved in the Civil War and the preservation of the Union. They will also study how Reconstruction and the Reconstruction Amendments to the U.S. Constitution began the move toward equality for African-Americans that came to the fore again nearly a century later, in the civil rights movement.

The reproducible student activities in this book draw students into this era of civil strife and rebuilding so they develop a rich understanding of these events that were so crucial to our national and racial history. Many activities in this book use original-source materials to make events that happened nearly a century and a half ago more immediate and accessible to students by sharing the thoughts and feelings of people who experienced them as contemporary life. Reading portions of original documents like the Fourteenth Amendment and the Emancipation Proclamation also brings these important texts to life for students.

Civil War soldier's mess kit

Organization

The student activity topics are divided into units guided by the National Standards for History. Each unit begins with several Student Background Pages that give the most relevant information on that unit's topic. A number of reproducible student activity pages follow, including reading selections from original contemporary sources and various analytical, interactive, and interdisciplinary activities.

Each unit includes some Extra Challenge activities to provide enrichment for more advanced or adventurous students. Time lines remind students of chronology, while inviting them into wider descriptive and illustrative areas. Maps are provided; you may make copies as needed for applicable activities.

Each unit is preceded by a Teacher Guide that gives an overview of the unit and its objectives, plus specific teaching suggestions for each student activity.

Lower-level students may have some difficulty reading original-source material, which contains some old-fashioned and higher-level words and syntax. You might want to go over some or all original-source selections in class to be sure all students fully understand them.

At the back of this book, the section titled Answers, Additional Activities, Assessments provides answers for the student activities, suggested additional activities, and at least one assessment vehicle for each unit. The resource section lists fiction and nonfiction books that will enrich students' learning and be helpful to you, plus media/computer research and enrichment resources. The glossary is reproducible for students' use.

TO THE STUDENT

The Civil War was a critical event in U.S. history. If the South had won, a previously united American nation would have been split in two. The United States of America would now be one country, and the Confederate States of America would be another. Fortunately for the United States, the North won the war. The nation stayed unified.

The Civil War began after southern states seceded—dropped out of the Union and formed their own nation, the Confederacy. What caused the southern states to take such a drastic step? Conflicts between the North and South had been simmering, sometimes boiling over, for years. During the 1850's, the question of slavery, especially in the western territories, drove North and South far apart.

The problems came to a head in 1860. Abraham Lincoln was the candidate of the antislavery Republican party. When Lincoln was elected, the southern states began to secede. When Confederate forces fired on a Union fort, the war began.

The Civil War was long, destructive, and terribly bloody. It left the South in ruins. The U.S. president and Congress wrangled bitterly over how to reconstruct (rebuild) the South, politically and socially. The dozen years following the Civil War are known as Reconstruction. During this time, former black slaves experienced some great changes in their lives. Southern society was reshaped. But by the end of Reconstruction, white domination of southern blacks was back in place.

The activities you'll be doing for this course of study will help you better understand this era of Civil War and Reconstruction. You'll work with maps and graphs. You'll put yourself in the shoes of this era's people, deciding what political party to support, discussing why (or why not) you'll enlist as a soldier, choosing a new direction for your life after being freed from slavery. You'll read what this era's people said about the great issues of their times. You'll learn what people—black and white, northern and southern—had to say about their daily lives. You'll read some original documents whose provisions still apply to your life today. At the end, you'll have a better grasp of these years that had such a large impact on our nation.

Focus on U.S. History:
The Era of the Civil War and Reconstruction

The Road to War

The objectives of this unit are to help students understand the sectional conflicts and differences between North and South and how they led to the Civil War. Although the Compromise of 1850 had settled some sectional differences, thorny problems remained. Southerners resented the steady stream of abolitionist propaganda, and they were outraged at the portrait of southern life painted in *Uncle Tom's Cabin*. Northerners were deeply angered by enforcement of the stronger Fugitive Slave Act. Most difficult was the issue of slavery in the western territories. The Kansas-Nebraska Act of 1854 let voters in those territories decide whether to be slave or free. This reversal of the Missouri Compromise so infuriated many Northerners that they formed a new antislavery political party, the Republican party. Violence broke out in Kansas between proslavery and antislavery forces. Then the Supreme Court in the Dred Scott case declared that the Missouri Compromise, banning slavery from certain territories, was unconstitutional. By the 1860 election, Northerners were convinced the South was aggressively trying to expand slavery throughout the West, and Southerners were convinced the rest of the country despised their region and was devoted to destroying their way of life. When Republican Abraham Lincoln won the presidential election of 1860, the Southern states decided the only way to protect themselves was to become independent. The Confederate States of America came into being in February 1861. On April 12, 1861, Confederate forces fired on the federal Fort Sumter in Charleston harbor, South Carolina, beginning the Civil War. This unit's activities are designed to draw students into a better understanding of the events along the road to civil war.

Student Activities

Mapping Slave and Free States familiarizes students with the alignment of slave and free states, Union and Confederacy.

Sectional Conflicts asks students to identify a number of sectional conflicts from 1850 to 1861 that drew North and South toward war. Students then use this information to create a time line, which they expand in subsequent units.

Political Parties and Their Stands provides students with a framework to differentiate among the Whig, Democratic, American (Know-Nothing), and Republican parties of the antebellum period, which also points up the growing sectional division in the country.

Which Party for You? has students imagine themselves as specific people of 1840's and 1850's America, then choosing which political party they support.

Graphing Election Results supplies statistics on popular and electoral votes in presidential elections from 1848 through 1860 for students to create a series of pie charts. Questions guide students in interpreting figures and charts.

North or South? is a group of thumbnail sketches of specific Americans. Students use their knowledge about differences between North and South to decide whether the person described is a Southerner or a Northerner. You could extend the activity by having students write their own thumbnail sketches and challenge classmates to identify the region.

The Dred Scott Decision highlights the main points of Chief Justice Taney's decision in this important case about slavery and states' rights. The second page is a framework for analyzing major details of the decision and its significance. For an Extra Challenge students read Taney's complete decision and then either read and summarize Justice Curtis's or write their own dissent in the case.

John Brown: The Man presents lyrics to the very popular (in the North) Civil War song "John Brown's Body," along with a quote from Brown about his motives. This material and the accompanying interpretive questions provide students with a springboard for writing a biographical sketch of Brown from an impartial, antislavery, or proslavery point of view.

Secession—Yes or No? lists arguments for and against secession made by politicians of the time. Students summarize major points for each side and then role-play a debate between supporters and opponents of secession.

A Pair of Presidents presents the different reactions of presidents Buchanan and Lincoln to southern secession in their own words. Students contrast and explain the two men's responses, ideally by writing a "contemporary" newspaper article.

A Lively Political Convention uses an 1860 newspaper report to convey the raucous nature of political party conventions in the mid-1800's. The activity sheet invites students to compare it with modern-day conventions they have seen or attended.

In **Party Platforms** students summarize where four political parties in the 1860 election stood on slavery in the territories based on excerpts from their party platforms.

In **The Confederate Constitution** students analyze certain clauses from the Constitution of the Confederate States of America to determine how (or if) each differs from the U.S. Constitution, which was the model for the Confederate Constitution.

Was the War Inevitable? finishes the unit with portions of Senator Seward's "irrepressible conflict" speech and Abraham Lincoln's "house divided" speech. Students answer interpretive questions about the speeches, then concluding with a class debate on whether the Civil War could have been avoided.

The Road to War

In the decades before the Civil War, tensions between North and South simmered steadily. The Compromise of 1850 had settled some sectional differences, but big problems remained.

- Southerners still wanted to bring slavery into the western territories.
- Enforcement of the new, stronger Fugitive Slave Act—forcing escaped blacks back to bondage—angered Northerners.
- Abolitionists (people who wanted an end to slavery) waged a propaganda war and interfered when fugitive slaves were captured. This, of course, angered Southerners.

Uncle Tom's Cabin

In 1852 the novel *Uncle Tom's Cabin* swept the country. It vividly portrayed the horrors of slavery—even though its writer, Harriet Beecher Stowe, had almost no firsthand knowledge of the topic. The novel greatly increased antislavery, anti-South feelings among Northerners. Southerners saw the book as an inaccurate, twisted attack on their way of life. Stowe had hoped the novel would promote a peaceful end to slavery. Instead, it divided the nation even more.

(continued)

The Road to War *(continued)*

The Kansas-Nebraska Act

North-South differences ran into each other head-on in Kansas. Both proslavery and antislavery settlers were pouring into this territory. It was time to set up a territorial government. Northern interests struck a deal with Southerners.

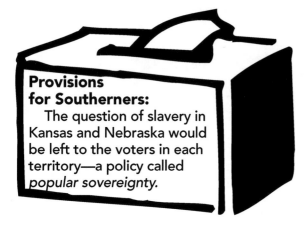

Provisions for Northerners:
A transcontinental railroad would be built along a northerly route.

Provisions for Southerners:
The question of slavery in Kansas and Nebraska would be left to the voters in each territory—a policy called *popular sovereignty*.

The Missouri Compromise had already banned slavery in the Kansas-Nebraska area. So, passage of the Kansas-Nebraska Act in 1854 totally outraged Northerners. Many switched to a radical antislavery stance. The newly formed Republican party, based on an antislavery policy, attracted members throughout the East and the Old Northwest (states like Ohio and Illinois, where the Northwest Ordinance had banned slavery since 1787).

"Bleeding Kansas"

Proslavery and antislavery forces turned Kansas into a battleground. "Border ruffians" from Missouri voted illegally and set up a proslavery government. They attacked the free town of Lawrence. John Brown and his followers killed proslavery settlers in revenge. The violence spilled over on the floor of the U.S. Senate. Congressman Preston Brooks, of South Carolina, beat Senator Charles Sumner, of Massachusetts, with a cane until he was unconscious in answer to the senator's antislavery speech "The Crime Against Kansas."

(continued)

The Road to War *(continued)*

The Supreme Court Steps In

In 1857, the U.S. Supreme Court issued a decision that deepened the North-South split yet more. Dred Scott, a black slave, sued for his freedom because he had lived with his master for a while in a free state and a free territory. The Court rejected Scott's claims. It said, first, that blacks were not citizens. It also declared that the Missouri Compromise was unconstitutional. Congress, the Court said, could not ban slavery from the territories.

> Dred Scott lost his case, but his master freed him soon after. He worked as a hotel porter in St. Louis and died in 1858, after just one year of freedom.

The gap between North and South widened. Many Northerners were now sure the South was aggressively trying to expand slavery throughout the West.

Presidential Politics

As you might expect, the North-South conflict expressed itself in the presidential elections. James Buchanan, representing the Democratic party and its policy of popular sovereignty, won the 1856 election. The Republicans made a strong showing, though, with their firm stand against slavery in the territories.

During the Illinois campaign for the Senate in 1858, a political newcomer rose to national attention. Republican Abraham Lincoln engaged in a series of debates against Stephen Douglas, the Democratic candidate. Lincoln focused the debates on the issue of slavery in the territories.

Lincoln lost the Senate election, but the Republican party had found its candidate for the 1860 presidential election. Democrats were deeply divided over the slavery question. A minor party fielded its own candidate. Here's how the 1860 presidential campaign looked:

| Republican Party: Abraham Lincoln | Democratic Party (North): Steven A. Douglas | Democratic Party (South): John C. Breckinridge | Constitutional Union Party: John Bell |

Lincoln emerged the winner.

(continued)

The Road to War *(continued)*

Secession, at Last

> One northern observer called South Carolina, the hotbed of secessionism, "too small for a republic and too large for an insane asylum."

Seven southern states responded to Lincoln's election by deciding to **secede**—leave the Union, stop being members of the United States. In their eyes, the election proved that the rest of the country despised the South and its way of life. To protect itself, the South needed to become independent, secessionists reasoned.

South Carolina was the first. By the day Lincoln took office in March 1861, seven southern states had seceded and formed a new nation, the Confederate States of America. The Confederacy started seizing federal property, including military posts, in the South. On April 12, 1861, Confederate forces started firing on Fort Sumter in Charleston harbor, South Carolina. Four more states immediately seceded. The Civil War had begun.

Time Line of Votes to Secede

December 1860	January 1861	February 1861	April 1861	May 1861
South Carolina	Georgia Florida Alabama Mississippi Louisiana	Texas	Virginia	Arkansas North Carolina Tennessee

Focus on U.S. History:
The Era of the Civil War and Reconstruction

Name _____

Date _____

Mapping Slave and Free States

Directions: Use the map below to show the following information. Use a different color for each group of states. Label each state with its name.

- Seven southern states that seceded and formed the Confederate States of America. Note dates of secession for each.
- Southern states that joined the Confederacy after the attack on Fort Sumter. Note secession dates for each.
- Union states that allowed slavery.
- Free Union states.

    Do the Union and Confederacy territories seem approximately equal or quite unequal?

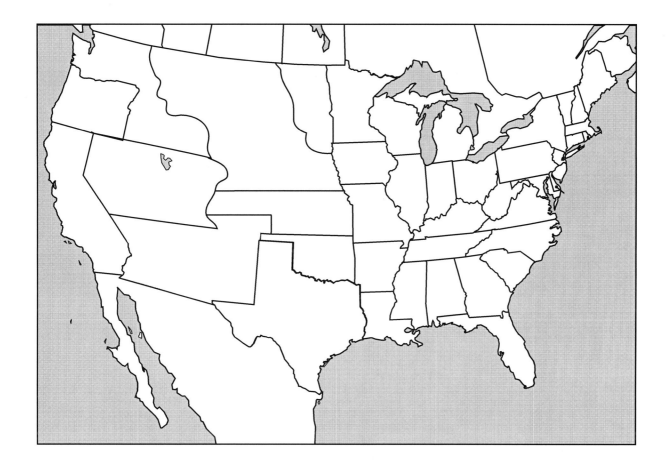

7

Focus on U.S. History:
The Era of the Civil War and Reconstruction

Sectional Conflicts

Many events from 1850 to 1861 drew the North and the South into civil war. Identify each event below. Give its date and describe briefly how it related to North-South problems. Then, use this information to create a time line of the road to civil war.

A best-selling novel sweeps the nation.	**A proslavery mob destroys a town.**
When? _____	When? _____
What? _____	What? _____
_____	_____
How? _____	How? _____
_____	_____
A new bill revives the controversy about slavery in the territories.	**Antislavery raiders capture a federal arsenal.**
When? _____	When? _____
What? _____	What? _____
_____	_____
How? _____	How? _____
_____	_____
An omnibus bill solves problems—temporarily.	**The Union loses its first member.**
When? _____	When? _____
What? _____	What? _____
_____	_____
How? _____	How? _____
_____	_____
Five proslavery settlers are killed.	**First shots of the Civil War are fired.**
When? _____	When? _____
What? _____	What? _____
_____	_____
How? _____	How? _____
_____	_____

(continued)

Focus on U.S. History:
The Era of the Civil War and Reconstruction

Sectional Conflicts *(continued)*

Antislavery politicians found a new political party.

When? _____

What? _____

_____

How? _____

_____

A new, stricter law angers Northerners.

When? _____

What? _____

_____

How? _____

_____

The Union loses five more states.

When? _____

What? _____

_____

How? _____

_____

State campaign debates draw national attention.

When? _____

What? _____

_____

How? _____

_____

Court rules: Slaves are not citizens.

When? _____

What? _____

_____

How? _____

_____

A new American nation is born.

When? _____

What? _____

_____

How? _____

_____

Vicious violence occurs in the U.S. Senate.

When? _____

What? _____

_____

How? _____

_____

A candidate unacceptable to the South wins a national election.

When? _____

What? _____

_____

How? _____

_____

Proslavery and antislavery constitutions compete.

When? _____

What? _____

_____

How? _____

_____

A Kentucky senator tries for a last compromise.

When? _____

What? _____

_____

How? _____

_____

Extra Challenge: You could add earlier slavery-related issues and events to your time line.
(See Book 4 of this series, *Focus on U.S. History: The Era of Expansion and Reform.*)

9   *Focus on U.S. History:*
                                                      The Era of the Civil War and Reconstruction

Political Parties and Their Stands

Directions: Political parties were forming and dissolving in the 1840's and 1850's. Identify their sources of support and where they stood on the main issues by completing the chart below. Do you see any indication of the growing sectional division in the nation?

Party (1840's and 1850's)	Section of Country Where Most Party Members Lived	Stand on Slavery in Existing States	Stand on Slavery in the Territories	Stand on Popular Sovereignty	Stand on Immigration
Whig					
Democratic					
American (Know-Nothing)					
Republican					

Challenge Questions:

1. Two minor parties of the 1840's were the Liberty Party and the Free Soil Party. How was the main policy for each of these parties different?

2. The Whig Party dissolved after the 1852 elections. What stand did each of these groups of Whigs take on slavery? Which party did these Whigs move to?

   (a) Cotton Whigs: _____

   (b) Conscience Whigs: _____

   (c) Silver Gray Whigs: _____

Focus on U.S. History:
The Era of the Civil War and Reconstruction

Which Party for You?

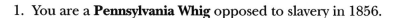

Directions: The United States had many political parties in the 1840's and 1850's. People dissatisfied with one moved to another or formed a new one. Imagine you are each of the people described below. Explain what political party you might choose to support.

1. You are a **Pennsylvania Whig** opposed to slavery in 1856.

2. You are an **antislavery Democrat** unhappy with the way your party is ducking the issues in 1848.

3. You are a **South Carolina slave owner** in the 1840's.

4. You are a **low-wage, native-born factory worker** in New York City in the 1850's.

5. You want to **vote for a candidate** in 1844 who favors the abolition of slavery.

6. You are a **Louisiana cotton grower** interested in expanding west of the Mississippi River.

7. You're a **Cotton Whig**, but your party is dissolving after 1852.

8. You're a **New Englander** transplanted to **Kansas** in the 1850's.

Name _____

Date _____

Graphing Election Results

Presidential elections in the years before the Civil War reflected growing sectional tensions. Here are popular vote totals for elections from 1848 through 1860.

Year	Candidate	Party	Popular Vote	Electoral Vote
1848	Zachary Taylor	Whig	1,360,101	163
	Lewis Cass	Democratic	1,220,544	127
	Martin Van Buren	Free Soil	291,263	0
1852	Franklin Pierce	Democratic	1,601,474	254
	Winfield Scott	Whig	1,386,578	42
1856	James Buchanan	Democratic	1,838,169	174
	John C. Frémont	Republican	1,335,264	114
	Millard Fillmore	American	874,534	8
1860	Abraham Lincoln	Republican	1,865,593	180
	Stephen A. Douglas	Democratic	1,382,713	12
	John C. Breckinridge	Democratic	848,356	72
	John Bell	Constitutional Union	592,906	39

Directions: Create graphs as directed below, and answer the questions.

1. From these figures, **create a series of pie charts** showing popular support for each party's candidates in the presidential contests, by year.

   Also, **calculate the percentage** of the total each candidate won and show this on your pie charts.

2. Which party disappeared from presidential elections after 1852? _____

   _____

3. What new party appeared in the 1856 and 1860 elections? _____

   _____

4. Why were there two Democratic candidates in the 1860 election? _____

   _____

5. What two groups came together to form the Free Soil Party? _____

   _____

6. What was the Constitutional Union Party? _____

   _____

Name _____

Date _____

North or South?

There were many social, economic, and cultural differences between North and South in the prewar years. Imagine you are each of the following people. Are you more likely to be a Northerner or a Southerner?

You're the mistress of a large plantation with many buildings. N/S? _____	You attend public school in your hometown. N/S? _____	You work in the vast coal fields of your native state. N/S? _____
You are a bookbinder worried that your former master may come looking for you. N/S? _____	You're a child who gets his education at home with a tutor. N/S? _____	You go to work at the age of seven or eight. N/S? _____
You're a male head of household very concerned about questions of honor and maintaining your region's way of life. N/S? _____	You're an Irish immigrant who lives in a city slum. N/S? _____	You've used your toolmaking skills to build and operate a machine tool factory. N/S? _____
You're a teenage girl who works in a textile mill and lives in a boarding house. N/S? _____	You're a teenage girl who spends her days in ladylike activities like arranging flowers. N/S? _____	You made a lot of money on your last whaling voyage. N/S? _____
Your children have been sent away from you forever. You had no say in the matter. N/S? _____	Your husband supports the family as a canal worker, while you care for the home and children. N/S? _____	You grow Bright Yellow tobacco on your tidewater farm. N/S? _____
You live in poverty in the backcountry mountains, unable to read, growing poor crops in the poor soil. N/S? _____	You and your husband operate a family wheat farm on the plains. N/S? _____	You've worked hard for wages since you were a youngster. Now you're a manufacturer of farm machinery. N/S? _____
You work in cotton fields from dawn to dusk. N/S? _____		

(continued)

Focus on U.S. History:
The Era of the Civil War and Reconstruction

The Dred Scott Decision

Dred Scott was a slave who sued for his freedom in federal court. His master had taken him to Illinois, a free state, and to Minnesota, a territory where slavery was forbidden by the Missouri Compromise of 1820. The Supreme Court's decision in this case had a tremendous impact across the nation.

Directions: Read these six excerpts from the decision of Chief Justice Roger Taney; then go on to the rest of this activity.

Dred Scott

Chief Justice Roger Taney, U.S. Supreme Court (1857)

The question is simply this: Can a Negro, whose ancestors were imported into this country, and sold as slaves, become a member of the political community formed and brought into existence by the Constitution of the United States, and as such become entitled to all the rights, and privileges, and immunities, guaranteed by that instrument to the citizen? One of which rights is the privilege of suing in a court of the United States. . . .

A Negro of the African race was regarded by [the American colonists] as an article of property, and held, and bought and sold as such, in every one of the thirteen colonies which united in the Declaration of Independence, and afterwards formed the Constitution of the United States. . . . It is too clear for dispute, that the enslaved African race were not intended to be included, and formed no part of, the people who framed and adopted the Declaration. . . .

The only two provisions [of the Constitution] which point to [Negroes] and include them, treat them as property, and make it the duty of the government to protect it. . . .

Upon a full and careful consideration of the subject, the court is of opinion, that, upon the facts stated . . . Dred Scott was not a citizen of Missouri within the meaning of the Constitution of the United States, and not entitled as such to sue in its courts. . . .

An Act of Congress which deprives a person of the United States of his liberty or property merely because he came himself or brought his property into a particular Territory of the United States, and who had committed no offense against the laws, could hardly be dignified with the name of due process of law. . . .

Upon these considerations, it is the opinion of the court that the Act of Congress which prohibited a citizen from holding and owning property of this kind in the Territory of the United States north of the line therein mentioned, is not warranted by the Constitution, and is therefore void.

(continued)

The Dred Scott Decision *(continued)*

Directions: From Chief Justice Taney's decision and background information about the case, use the framework on this page to analyze the details and significance of the Dred Scott decision.

- People involved in the lawsuit: _____

_____

- Three major questions of the case:

    1. _____

    2. _____

    3. _____

- Chief Justice Taney's decisions on those three questions:

    1. _____

    2. _____

    3. _____

- Outcome of the decision: _____

_____

- Impact of the decision in the North: _____

_____

- Impact of the decision in the South: _____

_____

Extra Challenge: Read Taney's complete decision in this case. Then do one of the following:

1. Read the dissent written by Justice Benjamin R. Curtis. Summarize his main points.

2. Write your own dissent to Taney's decision, responding to his main points.

Focus on U.S. History:
The Era of the Civil War and Reconstruction

John Brown: The Man

John Brown's raid on Harpers Ferry greatly alarmed southern slaveholders. A fiery fanatic who had hacked civilians to pieces in Kansas, Brown acted like a dignified martyr after his capture in Virginia. Here are some views of Brown.

Song: John Brown's Body

(to the tune of "The Battle Hymn of the Republic")

John Brown's body lies a-mould'ring in the ground,
John Brown's body lies a-mould'ring in the ground,
John Brown's body lies a-mould'ring in the ground,
But his soul goes marching on.

Chorus: Glory, glory, Hallelujah!
Glory, glory, Hallelujah!
Glory, glory, Hallelujah!
His soul goes marching on.

He's gone to be a soldier in the army of the Lord,
His soul goes marching on.—*Chorus*

John Brown died that the slave might be free,
But his soul goes marching on.—*Chorus*

They'll hang Jeff Davis on a sour apple tree,
As they go marching on.—*Chorus*

The stars of heaven are looking kindly down,
On the grave of old John Brown.—*Chorus*

Interviewed after his capture, Brown was asked, "Upon what principle do you justify your acts?"

Brown replied, "Upon the golden rule. I pity the poor in bondage that have none to help them; that is why I am here; not to gratify any personal animosity, revenge or vindictive spirit. It is my sympathy with the oppressed and the wronged, that are as good as you and as precious in the sight of God."

Question: Is this statement compatible with Brown's earlier statements and his actions in Kansas?

Question: Is this an accurate view of John Brown? What kind of song about John Brown might a proslavery Southerner compose?

Directions: Read more about Brown and write a biographical sketch of this contradictory man. Or write two biographical sketches of Brown, one by an antislavery Northerner and another by a proslavery Southerner. Add copies of political cartoons and artistic depictions of Brown to your sketch.

The Last Moments of John Brown,
by Thomas Hovenden, 1884

Secession—Yes or No?

The idea of states seceding from the Union was hotly debated. Should southern states secede? *Could* they do so legally? Here are some opinions of politicians at the time.

Alexander Hamilton Stephens, Georgia politician (later vice president of the Confederacy) (1860)

The first question that presents itself is, shall the people of Georgia secede from the Union in consequence of the election of Mr. Lincoln to the Presidency of the United States. My countrymen, I tell you frankly, candidly, and earnestly, that I do not think that they ought. . . . To make a point of resistance to the government, to withdraw from it because any man has been elected, would put us in the wrong. We are pledged to maintain the Constitution. . . . If all our hopes are to be blasted, if the Republic is to go down, let us be found to the last moment standing on the deck with the Constitution of the United States waving over our head. . . . We went into the election with this people. The result was different from what we wished; but the election has been constitutionally held. . . .

But it is said Mr. Lincoln's policy and principles are against the Constitution, and that, if he carries them out, it will be destructive of our rights. Let us not anticipate a threatened evil. If he violates the Constitution, then will come our time to act. . . .

[What is] the course which this state should pursue toward those northern states which . . . have attempted to nullify the Fugitive Slave Law? . . . Before making reprisals, we should exhaust every means of bringing about a peaceful settlement of the controversy. . . . At least, let these offending and derelict states know what your grievances are, and if they refuse, as I said, to give us our rights under the Constitution, I should be willing, as a last resort, to sever the ties of the Union with them.

Abraham Lincoln, president of the United States of America (1861)

I hold that, in contemplation of universal law and of the Constitution, the Union of these states is perpetual. Perpetuity is implied, if not expressed, in the fundamental law of all national governments.

Again, if the United States be not a government proper, but an association of states in the nature of contract merely, can it as a contract be peaceably unmade by less than all the parties who made it? One party to a contract may violate it—break it, so to speak; but does it not require all to lawfully rescind it?

Abraham Lincoln
(continued)

17

Focus on U.S. History:
The Era of the Civil War and Reconstruction

Secession—Yes or No? *(continued)*

Robert Toombs, senator from Georgia (1861)

The senator from Kentucky says he can find no constitutional right of secession. Perhaps not; but the Constitution is not the place to look for states' rights. If that right belongs to independent states, and they did not cede it to the federal government, it is reserved to the states, or to the people.

You [Northerners] say we shall submit to your construction [interpretation of the Constitution as forbidding secession]. We shall do it, if you can make us; but not otherwise, or in any other manner. That is settled. You may call it secession, or you may call it revolution; but there is a big fact standing before you, ready to oppose you—that fact is, freemen with arms in their hands. . . .

Then you have declared, Lincoln declares, our platform declares, you people declare, you Legislatures declare—there is one voice running

Robert Toombs

through your entire phalanx—that we [slave owners with slaves] shall be outlawed in the Territories of the United States. I say we will not be; and we are willing to meet the issue; and rather than submit to such an outlawry, we will defend our territorial rights as we would our household goods.

Louis Wigfall, senator from Texas (1861)

This federal government is dead. The only question is whether we will give it a decent, peaceable, Protestant burial, or whether we shall have an Irish wake at the grave. . . . Believing—no, sir, not believing, but knowing—that this Union is dissolved, never, never to be reconstructed upon any terms—not if you were to hand us blank paper, and ask us to write a constitution, would we ever again be confederated with you. . . . Then, knowing that the Union is dissolved, that reconstruction is impossible, I would, myself, had I been consulted by the Union-savers, have told them that Union-saving was impracticable, but that peaceable separation was practicable. . . .

A party has come into power that represents the antagonism to my own section of the country. It represents two million men who hate us, and who, by their votes for such a man as they have elected have committed an overt act of hostility. That they have done. . . . Our objection to living in this Union, and therefore the difficulty of reconstructing it, is . . . [that] you deny the sovereignty of the states; you deny the right of self-government in the people; you insist upon Negro equality; your people interfere impertinently with our institutions and attempt to subvert them; you . . . excite our slaves to insurrection against their masters, and . . . array one class of citizens against the other.

(continued)

Secession—Yes or No? *(continued)*

Jefferson Davis, president of the Confederate States of America (1861)

Jefferson Davis

Our present condition, achieved in a manner unprecedented in the history of nations, illustrates the American idea that governments rest upon the consent of the governed, and that it is the right of the people to alter or abolish governments whenever they become destructive of the ends for which they were established.

We have entered upon the career of independence, and it must be inflexibly pursued. Through many years of controversy with our late associates, the northern States, we have vainly endeavored to secure tranquillity and to obtain respect for the rights to which we were entitled. As a necessity, not a choice, we have resorted to the remedy of separation.

Directions: In the space provided below, summarize, in list form, the major points made by people for and against secession. Then use your list to role-play with classmates a debate between supporters and opponents of secession from the Union by southern states.

Arguments for Secession	**Arguments Against Secession**

Focus on U.S. History:
The Era of the Civil War and Reconstruction

A Pair of Presidents

The first southern states seceded while James Buchanan was still president of the United States. More seceded after Abraham Lincoln took the oath of office. The two men had different reactions to secession. Here's what they said about it.

James Buchanan, president of the United States (1860)

The question fairly stated is: Has the Constitution delegated to Congress the power to coerce a state into submission which is attempting to withdraw or has actually withdrawn from the Confederacy? If answered in the affirmative, it must be on the principle that the power has been conferred upon Congress to declare and to make war against a state. After much serious reflection, I have arrived at the conclusion that no such power has been delegated to Congress or to any other department of the federal government. . . .

But if we possessed this power, would it be wise to exercise it under existing circumstances? . . . War would not only present the most effectual means of destroying [the Union], but it would banish all hope of its peaceable reconstruction . . . rendering future reconciliation between the states impossible.

James Buchanan

Abraham Lincoln, president of the United States (1861)

I . . . consider that, in view of the Constitution and the laws, the Union is unbroken; and to the extent of my ability I shall take care, as the Constitution itself expressly enjoins upon me, that the laws of the Union be faithfully executed in all the states. . . . I trust this will not be regarded as a menace, but only as the declared purpose of the Union that it will constitutionally defend and maintain itself. . . .

In your hands, my dissatisfied fellow-countrymen, and not in mine, is the momentous issue of civil war. The government will not assail you. You can have no conflict without being yourselves the aggressors. You have no oath registered in heaven to destroy the government, while I shall have the most solemn one to "preserve, protect, and defend" it.

Abraham Lincoln

Directions: From what you have read, explain the differences between Buchanan's and Lincoln's responses to southern secession. You could do this in the form of a newspaper article written after Lincoln delivered his first inaugural address (quoted above), comparing Lincoln's response with what Buchanan said in his message to Congress in December 1860 (quoted above).

A Lively Political Convention

Directions: Back in the 1800's, political conventions weren't the dull, scripted events we know today. Read this description of the Republican party convention of 1860, penned by newspaper reporter Murat Halstead. Then compare it with a modern-day national, state, or local convention you've attended or watched on TV.

When the convention was called to order, breathless attention was given the proceedings. There was not a space a foot square in the wigwam [hall] unoccupied.

The applause, when Mr. Evarts named Seward, was enthusiastic. When Mr. Judd named Lincoln, the response was prodigious, rising and ranging far beyond the Seward shriek. Presently, upon Caleb B. Smith seconding the nomination of Lincoln, the response was absolutely terrific.

It now became the Seward men to make another effort, and when Blair of Michigan seconded his nomination, there rose a wild yell. The effect was startling. Hundreds of persons stopped their ears in pain. The shouting was absolutely frantic, shrill and wild. No Comanches, no panthers ever struck a higher note, or gave screams with more infernal intensity. Looking from the stage over the vast amphitheater, nothing was to be seen below but thousands of hats—a black, mighty swarm of hats—flying with the velocity of hornets over a mass of human heads, most of the mouths of which were open. Above, all around the galleries, hats and handkerchiefs were flying in the tempest together. . . .

Now the Lincoln men had to try it again, and as Mr. Delano . . . seconded the nomination of Lincoln, the uproar was beyond description. . . . I thought the Seward yell could not be surpassed; but the Lincoln boys were clearly ahead, and feeling their victory, as there was a lull in the storm, took deep breaths all round, and gave a concentrated shriek that was positively awful, and accompanied it with stamping that made every plank and pillar in the building quiver.

Focus on U.S. History:
The Era of the Civil War and Reconstruction

Party Platforms

The political parties of 1860 were very concerned about the question of slavery in the territories. Here are parts of their various **platforms**—the policies they supported.

Democratic Party (Douglas Faction):

Inasmuch as difference of opinion exists in the Democratic party as to the nature and extent of the powers of a Territorial Legislature, and as to the powers and duties of Congress, under the Constitution of the United States, over the institution of slavery within the Territories,

Resolved, that the Democratic party will abide by the decision of the Supreme Court of the United States upon these questions of Constitutional Law.

Democratic Party (Breckenridge Faction):

Resolved . . . That the Government of a Territory organized by an act of Congress is provisional and temporary, and during its existence all citizens of the United States have an equal right to settle with their property in the Territory, without their rights, either of person or property, being destroyed or impaired by Congressional or territorial legislation.

Republican Party:

Resolved . . . That the new dogma that the Constitution, of its own force, carries slavery into any or all of the Territories of the United States, is a dangerous political heresy, at variance with the explicit provisions of that instrument itself, with contemporaneous exposition, and with legislative and judicial precedent; is revolutionary in its tendency and subversive of the peace and harmony of the country.

That the normal condition of all the territory of the United States is that of freedom . . . and we deny the authority of Congress, of a territorial legislature, or of any individuals, to give legal existence to slavery in any territory of the United States.

Constitutional Union Party

Resolved, that it is both the part of patriotism and of duty to recognize no political principle other than THE CONSTITUTION OF THE COUNTRY, THE UNION OF THE STATES, AND THE ENFORCEMENT OF THE LAWS.

Directions: Summarize the position of each of these party platforms on the issue of slavery in the territories.

1. Republican party: _____

2. Democratic party (Douglas): _____

3. Democratic party (Breckenridge):_____

4. Constitutional Union party: _____

Focus on U.S. History:
The Era of the Civil War and Reconstruction

The Confederate Constitution

Directions: The Constitution of the Confederate States of America was modeled after the Constitution of the United States, with some changes. For each provision of the Confederate Constitution below, tell how (or if) it is different from the U.S. Constitution.

> Representatives . . . shall be apportioned among the several states . . . according to their respective numbers, which shall be determined by adding to the whole number of free persons . . . three-fifths of all slaves.

Differences (if any): _____

_____

> The importation of Negroes of the African race, from any foreign country . . . is hereby forbidden; and Congress is required to pass such laws as shall effectually prevent the same.

Differences (if any): _____

_____

> The executive power shall be vested in a president of the Confederate States of America. He and the vice-president shall hold their offices for the term of six years; but the president shall not be reeligible.

Differences (if any): _____

_____

> No slave or other person held to service or labor in any state or territory of the Confederate States . . . escaping or unlawfully carried into another, shall . . . be discharged from such service or labor; but shall be delivered up on claim of the party to whom such slave belongs, or to whom such service or labor may be due.

Differences (if any): _____

_____

(continued)

The Confederate Constitution *(continued)*

> Congress shall have power to legislate and provide governments for the inhabitants of all territory belonging to the Confederate States. . . . In all such territory, the institution of Negro slavery, as it now exists in the Confederate States, shall be recognized and protected by Congress and by the territorial government; and the inhabitants of the several Confederate states and territories shall have the right to take to such territory any slaves lawfully held by them in any of the states or territories of the Confederate States.

Differences (if any): _____

_____

> No . . . law denying or impairing the right of property in Negro slaves shall be passed.

Differences (if any): _____

_____

Extra Challenge: Draw up a constitution for an elected student assembly for your school. Be sure to include rules for who is eligible to be elected, who is eligible to vote, how often elections will be held, and what powers the assembly will have. Make notes for your new constitution in the space below.

Was the War Inevitable?

Could the Civil War have been avoided, especially as late as 1860 and 1861?
Two prominent national leaders gave speeches about this. Here's what they had to say.

Senator William Henry Seward (1858)

Our country is a theater, which exhibits, in full operation, two radically different political systems; the one resting on the basis of servile or slave labor, the other on the basis of voluntary labor of freemen. . . .

The two systems are at once perceived to be incongruous. But they are more than incongruous—they are incompatible. They never have permanently existed together in one country, and they never can. . . .

Increase of population, which is filling the states out to their very borders, together with a new and extended network of railroads and other avenues, and an internal commerce which daily becomes more intimate, is rapidly bringing the states into a higher and more perfect social unity or consolidation. Thus, these antagonistic systems are continually coming into closer contact, and collision results.

William Henry Seward

Shall I tell you what this collision means? They who think that it is accidental, unnecessary, the work of interested or fanatical agitators, and therefore ephemeral, mistake the case altogether. It is an irrepressible conflict between opposing and enduring forces, and it means that the United States must and will, sooner or later, become either entirely a slave-holding nation, or entirely a free-labor nation. Either the cotton and rice fields of South Carolina and the sugar plantations of Louisiana will ultimately be tilled by free labor, and Charleston and New Orleans become marts for legitimate merchandise alone, or else the rye-fields and wheat-fields of Massachusetts and New York must again be surrendered by their farmers to slave culture and to the production of slaves, and Boston and New York become once more markets for trade in the bodies and souls of men. It is the failure to apprehend this great truth that induces so many unsuccessful attempts at final compromise between the slave and free states, and it is the existence of this great fact that renders all such pretended compromises, when made, vain and ephemeral. . . .

I know, and you know, that a revolution has begun. I know, and all the world knows, that revolutions never go backward. . . . While the government of the United States, under the conduct of the Democratic party, has been all [this] time surrendering one plain and castle after another to slavery, the people of the United States have been no less steadily and perseveringly gathering together the forces with which to recover back again all the fields and all the castles which have been lost, and to confound and overthrow, by one decisive blow, the betrayers of the Constitution and Freedom forever.

(continued)

*Focus on U.S. History:
The Era of the Civil War and Reconstruction*

Was the War Inevitable? *(continued)*

Abraham Lincoln (1858)

If we could first know where we are, and whither we are tending, we could better judge what to do, and how to do it. We are now far into the fifth year since a policy was initiated with the avowed object and confident promise of putting an end to slavery agitation. Under the operation of that policy, that agitation has not only not ceased, but has constantly augmented. In my opinion, it will not cease until a crisis shall have been reached and passed.

"A house divided against itself cannot stand." I believe this government cannot endure permanently half slave and half free. I do not expect the Union to be dissolved—I do not expect the house to fall—but I do expect it will cease to be divided. It will become all one thing, or all the other. Either the opponents of slavery will arrest the further spread of it, and place it where the public mind shall rest in the belief that it is in the course of ultimate extinction; or its advocates will push it forward till it shall become alike lawful in all the states, old as well as new, North as well as South.

Abraham Lincoln

Directions: Answer the questions; then debate as directed below.

1. What metaphor (figure of speech) does Lincoln use to dramatize the current national situation?

   _____

2. What metaphor does Seward use to dramatize the gains and losses of the antislavery and proslavery sides? _____

   _____

3. What argument do both Lincoln and Seward make about the possibility of war?

   _____

   _____

4. Think over what you have read and studied about the events leading up to the Civil War and what people of those times wrote and said about what was happening. Then take part in a class debate on this question: **Was the Civil War inevitable, or could it have been avoided?**

Fighting the War

The objectives of this unit are to help students understand important factors that affected the course of the Civil War and the reasons for the North's victory. As the war began, the industrial North had many advantages over the agricultural South. The North had a much larger population, many more manufacturing plants, thousands more miles of railroads, control of the nation's money, and a strong navy. The South, however, had excellent commanders and was fighting on familiar land in defense of its own homes and families. In the war's early years, the North suffered from inept, indecisive commanders. In the beginning, both sides expected an easy victory; shockingly high casualty figures from hard-fought battles of 1862 erased those notions. At first, President Lincoln presented the war as a fight to save the Union. By September of 1862 he added ending slavery as a purpose for war. His Emancipation Proclamation took effect in January 1863. The war tide turned for the North with victories at Gettysburg and Vicksburg in July 1863. Sherman marched a swath of destruction through Georgia then swept north to join Grant in forcing the shrinking southern army under Lee to surrender at Appomattox Court House on April 9, 1865. This unit's activities are designed to draw your students into a better understanding of the course of the war.

Student Activities

Mapping the War familiarizes students with sites and dates of major battles. The Extra Challenge asks students to give alternate names for some battles.

Strengths and Weaknesses lists particular advantages and disadvantages in the war and asks students to identify whether each applies to North or South and to explain how it helped or hurt that side.

The Call for Volunteers asks students to identify the emotional and practical appeals a recruiting ad used to attract volunteer soldiers. For an extra challenge students can compare this ad with another one from the Mexican War in book 4 of this series, *Focus on U.S. History: The Era of Expansion and Reform.*

Divided Loyalties quotes Robert E. Lee describing the difficulties of his decision to resign from the Union army and align himself with his native Virginia. Students role-play a dialogue between Lee and his sister, a Union supporter, about Lee's choice.

The Technology of War pictures new technology used in this "first modern war." Students identify each item and tell how it was used and how it affected the war.

The Battles lists the war's major battles. Students supply the date and casualty figures for each battle, where available (underlining the dreadful human toll of the war for both sides), and explain how each battle affected the course of the war.

Reporting the War shows how newspapers of the Civil War era used dramatic headlines in series to report on battles. Students create their own dramatic headline series, modeled on the real series, for the Civil War battle of their choice. Headlines can be combined to create a lively classroom or hallway display.

Mapping a Campaign uses Union and Confederate forces' actions in Virginia at the war's end to give students a sense of the movements and maneuvering involved in the war's conduct.

Who Am I? strengthens students' knowledge of Civil War leaders by having them read descriptions of individuals aloud and compete in teams to answer "Who am I?" Students could extend this activity by creating more description cards themselves.

The Emancipation Proclamation quotes Lincoln's proclamation and then uses interpretive questions to help students understand its provisions, why Lincoln issued it, and how it was received in the North and the South. In the Extra Challenge students locate and copy individual black slaves' reactions to the proclamation.

Graphing the War uses a North-South population bar graph and a troop strength line graph. Students answer a series of questions about the graphs that reveal disparities in population and troop strength between North and South. Students also use a casualties chart to create pie charts showing the large number of casualties suffered by both sides in the war.

Time Line of the War has students continue the Civil War time line they started in Unit 1, adding events from The Battles activity completed earlier in this unit and events listed on this activity sheet.

The Gettysburg Address presents Lincoln's famous speech in its entirety. Students discuss what makes this such an effective, memorable speech and explore what relevance it may have today.

The *Monitor* and the *Merrimac* uses a dramatic eyewitness account to bring the world's first battle between ironclad ships to life. Students are invited to imagine themselves in the midst of the battle.

Entrance of the 55th Massachusetts Regiment to Charleston

Fighting the War

North vs. South

On the brink of war, how did the North and South stack up against each other? Each had strengths and weaknesses, but the North had a tremendous edge.

Northern Strengths

- Much greater population
- Manufactured nine times more than the South—army would be well supplied
- 13,000 more miles of railroad tracks
- Controlled most of the nation's money
- Strong navy

Northern Weaknesses

- Divided public opinion at home
- Troops fighting away from home, in unfamiliar territory and climate
- Inept, indecisive commanders at first

Southern Strengths

- Defending own homes, families, land
- Skilled, effective commanders
- United, highly motivated
- Fighting in familiar country

Southern Weaknesses

- Agricultural economy—few supplies for war; income depended on exports
- No army at first, and no navy
- No national government at first
- Few major railroad lines
- Small population, many of whom were slaves

(continued)

Fighting the War *(continued)*

The War Begins

The onset of war posed difficult dilemmas for many Americans. Southern officers in the U.S. Army who chose to serve the Confederacy had to break their solemn oath of loyalty to the Union. Families were divided, especially in the border states. Missouri, Maryland, and Kentucky were slave states that elected to remain in the Union. Many of their citizens opted to fight for the Union.

Mary Todd Lincoln was the wife of the U.S. president. Members of her family supported the Confederacy. The brother of Varina Davis, wife of the Confederate president, fought in the Union Army.

Mary Todd Lincoln

Fighting the War: The Early Years

Jefferson Davis, president of the Confederacy, faced enormous difficulties. He had to create an army *and* a national government for states that were fighting for states' rights. Abraham Lincoln had to contend with poor military leaders until he discovered Ulysses S. Grant. He had to balance pro-slavery and abolitionist sentiments within the Union. His strength, determination, and thoughtfulness ultimately held the nation together.

Jefferson Davis

Sam Houston, of Texas, said Jefferson Davis was "as cold as a lizard and as ambitious as Lucifer."

Both North and South expected a swift, easy victory as the war began. Northern notions were shattered at the first big battle, Bull Run, in July 1861. Confederate forces drove panicked Union troops back to Washington—along with fleeing spectators. The Rebels lost hope of an easy win at the Battle of Shiloh in April 1862, when the South had to retreat after an initial victory. Both sides were badly shaken by the enormous losses at Shiloh, a total of over 25,000 casualties. Even the people at home, far from the battlefield, now realized that this war wasn't a romantic adventure.

Shiloh is a Hebrew word for "place of peace."

The war didn't go well for the North in 1862. Confederates, under their superb commander Robert E. Lee, bested the Union forces in Maryland and Virginia led by George McClellan, ever slow to act. However, in September 1862 the shockingly bloody battle of Antietam, in Maryland, forced Lee to end his first invasion of northern territory.

(continued)

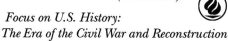

Fighting the War *(continued)*

The Emancipation Proclamation

Lincoln seized on the "victory" (actually a draw) at Antietam to make a bold move. He issued a first **Emancipation Proclamation**. As of January 1, 1863, slaves "in areas still in rebellion" would become free.

> **General Robert E. Lee** on war: "It is well that war is so terrible—we would grow too fond of it."

At first, Lincoln had insisted that the purpose of the war was to save the Union. Now, though, he felt northern public opinion was ready to accept ending slavery as another reason for the war. Also, freeing the slaves would rob the South of its labor pool and provide new soldiers for the North. Across the South, whenever Union troops appeared, slaves rushed eagerly to their lines.

The War Tide Turns

Union forces suffered several more dreadful defeats, at Fredericksburg in December 1862 and at Chancellorsville in May 1863. Then the momentum changed. Lee invaded the North once again. He was turned back at the climatic July 1863 battle of Gettysburg in Pennsylvania. The next day, Vicksburg, Mississippi, yielded to General Grant's siege.

That was the turning point of the war. The Union now began to grind the Confederates down with superior strength and numbers. Lee's broken army retreated back to Virginia. Vicksburg's fall put the Union in control of the Mississippi River, which crippled southern trade.

In the east, Grant battled Lee. Casualties on both sides were terrible, but the South suffered more—and it

> **General William Sherman** on war: "It is all hell."

was running out of replacements. Farther south, General William Sherman marched his troops across Georgia, destroying the southern countryside in a swath 60 miles wide. Atlanta fell to Sherman in September 1864.

After Atlanta, President Lincoln's popularity soared in the North. Southerners were demoralized, staggering. Sherman marched north to Virginia, where Grant was relentlessly pressuring Lee and his dwindling troops. Finally, Lee decided that further bloodshed was futile. He surrendered at Appomattox Court House, Virginia, on April 9, 1865.

Robert E. Lee's surrender at Appomattox, 1865

Name _____

Date _____

Map: Civil War Battles

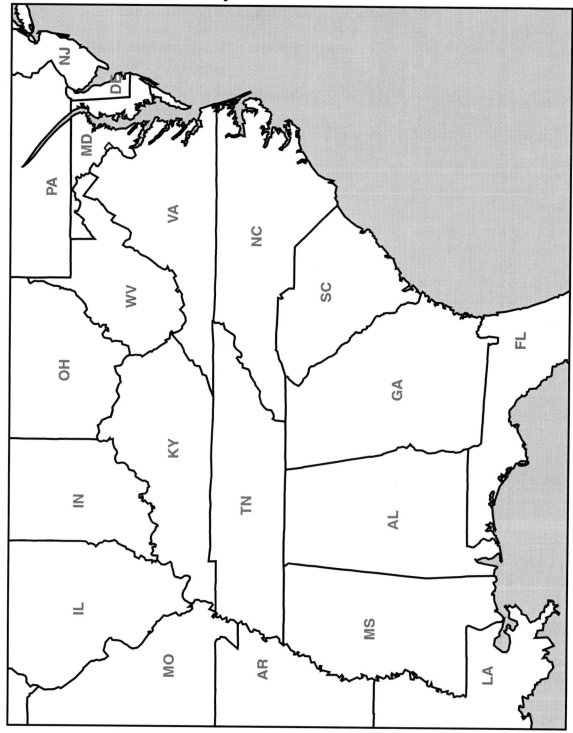

Focus on U.S. History:
The Era of the Civil War and Reconstruction

Mapping the War

Directions: Locate and label the following battle sites on your map of Civil War battles.

- Show the date(s) of each.
- Mark sites in three different colors: blue for a northern victory, gray for a southern victory, red for no clear victory on either side.
- Trace Sherman's swath of destruction through the South.

Battle Sites	Cities Taken by Sherman/Grant
Battle Sites	**Cities Taken by Sherman/Grant**
Fort Sumter	Atlanta
First Battle of Bull Run	Savannah
Fort Donelson	Columbia
Shiloh	Richmond
Seven Days' Campaign	
Second Battle of Bull Run	
Antietam	
Fredericksburg	
Chancellorsville	
Gettysburg	
Vicksburg siege	
Wilderness	
Spotsylvania Court House	
Cold Harbor	
Petersburg siege	

Civil War battle

Extra Challenge: Some of these battles have alternate names. Write them in parentheses after the names given above. What accounts for these differences?

Strengths and Weaknesses

Directions: Both North and South entered the war with certain strengths and weaknesses. Tell whether each strength or weakness described below applies to the North or to the South. Then explain how it helps or hurts that region.

1. **Has an agricultural economy.**   N/S? _____

   How helps/hurts: _____

   _____

2. **Has a sharp sense of having been wronged.**   N/S? _____

   How helps/hurts: _____

   _____

3. **Controls most of the nation's money.**   N/S? _____

   How helps/hurts: _____

   _____

4. **Has 70 percent of the nation's railroads.**   N/S? _____

   How helps/hurts: _____

   _____

5. **Is led from the beginning by smart, able generals.**   N/S? _____

   How helps/hurts: _____

   _____

(continued)

Strengths and Weaknesses *(continued)*

6. **Is fighting far from home.   N/S?** _____

   How helps/hurts: _____

   _____

7. **Has nine times as many factories as the other region.   N/S?** _____

   How helps/hurts: _____

   _____

8. **Is fighting to defend and hold home ground.   N/S?** _____

   How helps/hurts: _____

   _____

9. **Controls both the merchant marine and the federal navy.   N/S?** _____

   How helps/hurts: _____

   _____

10. **Has a strongly united home front.   N/S?** _____

    How helps/hurts: _____

    _____

11. **Believes strongly in states' rights.   N/S?** _____

    How helps/hurts: _____

    _____

12. **Has no national government at first.   N/S?** _____

    How helps/hurts: _____

    _____

The Call for Volunteers

Directions: At first, Civil War soldiers were volunteers. Here's a typical recruiting ad. In the spaces provided below, identify the emotional and practical appeals the ad uses to get men to become soldiers in the war.

Recruits Wanted

FOR THE

TWENTIETH IOWA INFANTRY.

RECRUITING OFFICE HAS BEEN OPENED OVER

Jordan's Store.

YOUNG MEN OF IOWA, now is the time to make yourselves known and felt. Shoulder the musket and off for the war, and leave the task of suppressing traitors at home to the aged and infirm, while you go forth to battle for your country's freedom, and win for yourselves

Imperishable Honor and Glory.

Pay and subsistence to commence from date of enlistment.
Twenty-five dollars of the $100 bounty and one month's pay
WILL BE PAID IN ADVANCE.

CAPT. CHESTER BARNEY, Recruiting officer

Nationalistic appeals: **Economic appeals:**

_____   _____

_____   _____

Quality-of-life appeals:

_____

Extra Challenge: Compare this recruiting poster with the Mexican War recruiting poster on page 16 of book 4 of this series, *Focus on U.S. History: The Era of Expansion and Reform.* What similar visual and written appeals do these ads use? How are the ads different?

Divided Loyalties

When war broke out, southern and northern men had to decide which army to serve in. No one agonized more over this choice than Robert E. Lee. Lee was a West Point graduate and a lieutenant colonel in the U.S. Army. In April 1861, President Lincoln offered Lee the command of the northern army, but Lee's native state of Virginia had just seceded. Lee described his difficult decision in several letters. Here are some excerpts.

I see only that a fearful calamity [secession] is upon us. There is no sacrifice I am not ready to make for the preservation of the Union save that of honor. If a disruption takes place, I shall go back in sorrow to my people and share the misery of my native state.

I declined the offer [from President Lincoln to command the northern army], stating, as candidly and courteously as I could, that though opposed to secession and deprecating war, I could take no part in an invasion of the southern states.

It has been a struggle to separate myself from a service to which I have devoted all the best years of my life [resigning from the U.S. Army].

With all my devotion to the Union and the feeling of loyalty and duty of an American citizen, I have not been able to make up my mind to raise my hand against my relatives, my children, my home. I have therefore resigned my commission in the Army, and save in defense of my native state (with the sincere hope that my poor services may never be needed), I hope I may never be called upon to draw my sword.

Lee's hopes were not realized. Days after he resigned from the U.S. Army, Virginia called him to lead its army.

Directions: Lee's sister was a Union supporter. Write or role-play a dialogue between Lee and Anne Lee Marshall about whether Lee should remain with the Union army or resign and, if he resigns, whether he should join the Confederate army and fight against his former comrades.

Robert E. Lee

The Technology of War

The Civil War is called the "first modern war." New technology used in this war changed the way all future wars would be fought.

Directions: Identify these new items of military technology, and tell how they affected the war.

What: _____

Use/effect: _____

_____

What: _____

Use/effect: _____

_____

What: _____

Use/effect: _____

_____

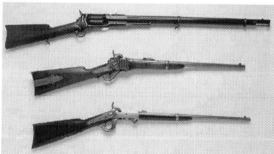

What: _____

Use/effect: _____

_____

(continued)

The Technology of War (continued)

What: _____

Use/effect: _____

_____

What: _____

Use/effect: _____

_____

What: _____

Use/effect: _____

_____

What: _____

Use/effect: _____

_____

Focus on U.S. History:
The Era of the Civil War and Reconstruction

The Battles

Directions: We can trace the progress of the Civil War through its major battles. For each battle listed below, give the date, the number of casualties on each side (where figures are available), and the effect it had on the war as a whole, on the North, and on the South.

1. **Fort Sumter**   Date: _____

   Casualties: North: _____   South: _____

   Effect: _____

   _____

2. **First Battle of Bull Run**   Date: _____

   Casualties: North: _____   South: _____

   Effect: _____

   _____

3. **Fort Donelson**   Date: _____

   Casualties: North: _____   South: _____

   Effect: _____

   _____

4. **La Glorieta Pass**   Date: _____

   Casualties: North: _____   South: _____

   Effect: _____

   _____

5. **Shiloh**   Date: _____

   Casualties: North: _____   South: _____

   Effect: _____

   _____

6. **Seven Days' Campaign**   Date: _____

   Casualties: North: _____   South: _____

   Effect: _____

   _____

7. **Second Battle of Bull Run**   Date: _____

   Casualties: North: _____   South: _____

   Effect: _____

(continued)

Focus on U.S. History:
The Era of the Civil War and Reconstruction

The Battles (continued)

8. **Antietam**   Date: _____

   Casualties: North: _____   South: _____

   Effect: _____

   _____

9. **Fredericksburg**   Date: _____

   Casualties: North: _____   South: _____

   Effect: _____

   _____

10. **Stones River**   Date: _____

    Casualties: North: _____   South: _____

    Effect: _____

    _____

11. **Chancellorsville**   Date: _____

    Casualties: North: _____   South: _____

    Effect: _____

    _____

12. **Gettysburg**   Date: _____

    Casualties: North: _____   South: _____

    Effect: _____

    _____

13. **Vicksburg, siege and fall**   Date: _____

    Effect: _____

    _____

14. **Chickamauga**   Date: _____

    Casualties: North: _____   South: _____

    Effect: _____

    _____

15. **Chattanooga**   Date: _____

    Casualties: North: _____   South: _____

    Effect: _____

    _____

(continued)

The Battles (continued)

16. **Wilderness**   Date: _____

Casualties: North: _____   South: _____

Effect: _____

_____

17. **Spotsylvania Court House**   Date: _____

Casualties: North: _____   South: _____

Effect: _____

_____

18. **Cold Harbor**   Date: _____

Casualties: North: _____   South: _____

Effect: _____

_____

19. **Fall of Atlanta and Sherman's march**   Date: _____

Effect: _____

_____

20. **Fall of Richmond and Petersburg**   Date: _____

Effect: _____

_____

Pickett's Charge, The Battle of Gettysburg

*Focus on U.S. History:
The Era of the Civil War and Reconstruction*

Reporting the War

Many newspapers of the Civil War era shouted the day's war news in a series of dramatic head-lines. Here's how the *Davenport Daily Gazette* (Iowa) headlined several battle stories in 1863. The headlines provide a dramatic summary of the stories' major points. Different type styles and sizes make the page more interesting.

Directions: Read a detailed description of a Civil War battle that seems particularly dramatic and interesting to you. Then create a series of headlines for a newspaper story about the battle. Be sure to use a variety of type styles and sizes in your headlines. You and your classmates will combine headlines for a classroom or hallway display.

Mapping a Campaign

Directions: Generals in the war tried to plan connected series of operations when they could. To get a sense of the two armies' movements and maneuvering, trace the final phase of the war on the map below.

- Use two different colors to show the movements of Grant's Union forces and Lee's Confederate forces as they meet at:

the Wilderness	Totopotomoy Creek
Spotsylvania Court House	Cold Harbor
North Anna River	Petersburg

- Continue to show the movement of Union and Confederate forces from Richmond and Petersburg to the final surrender at Appomattox Court House.
- Show dates of battles and sieges.

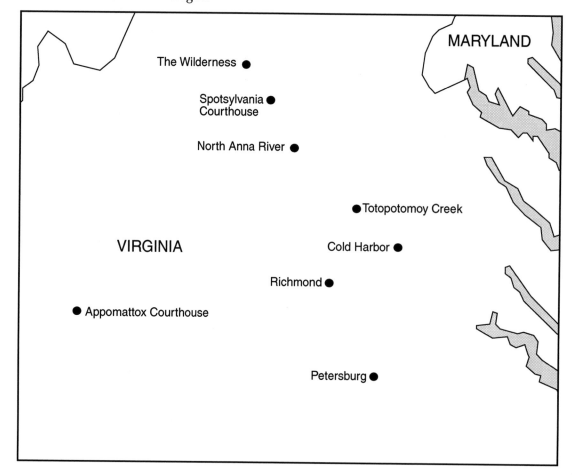

Focus on U.S. History:
The Era of the Civil War and Reconstruction

Name _____

Date _____

Who Am I?

Directions: Form teams, cut out these cards, and play a Who Am I? game. Or ask questions in a *Jeopardy!*-style game. Teams take turns drawing cards and reading them aloud. Can the other team answer correctly?

???

When urged to take away this general's command, President Lincoln replied, "I can't spare this man. He fights." Nickname: Unconditional Surrender. *Who am I?* Ulysses S. Grant	Superb at getting his green troops trained as soldiers, he was maddeningly reluctant to go into battle. Nickname: The Virginia Creeper. *Who am I?* George McClellan
A master at battle strategy, his men revered him. *Who am I?* Robert E. Lee	Dashing cavalry leader fond of plumed hats and flowing cloaks; he let Lee down, perhaps critically, at Gettysburg. *Who am I?* J.E.B. Stuart
He's the man Robert E. Lee depended on as his second in command—"Old Pete"—or, as Lee said, "my old war horse." *Who am I?* James Longstreet	College professor whose startling bayonet charge saved the battle of Gettysburg and possibly, therefore, the Union. *Who am I?* Joshua Lawrence Chamberlain
Likable, big, friendly man whose whiskers gave a name to an enduring style. *Who am I?* Ambrose E. Burnside	He held his men fast at the first battle of Bull Run and so earned the nickname of a rock wall. *Who am I?* Thomas J. Jackson (Stonewall)

(continued)

© 1997 J. Weston Walch, Publisher

45

Focus on U.S. History:
The Era of the Civil War and Reconstruction

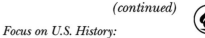

Who Am I? (continued)

???

A believer in total warfare and a plain speaker, he said of war, "It is all hell." Nickname: Uncle Billy. *Who am I?* William T. Sherman	Military genius, a cavalry commander, who later became a leader of the Ku Klux Klan. *Who am I?* Nathan Bedford Forrest
Dashing, gallant cavalry commander who led a wild raid through Ohio. *Who am I?* John Hunt Morgan	"Little Pete" led his forces as they destroyed the Shenandoah Valley of Virginia. *Who am I?* Philip Sheridan
The "Napoleon of the South," who directed his troops to a big, early win at Bull Run/Manassas. *Who am I?* Pierre G.T. Beauregard	Vain, bad-tempered general, he commanded at Gettysburg but failed to attack the retreating Confederate forces and finish them off. *Who am I?* George Meade
Last name shared by two Confederate leaders, one who won at Shiloh and another who commanded at Seven Pines. *Who am I?* Joseph E. Johnston Albert Sidney Johnston	"Fighting Joe" had a bad temper and an arrogant air; Lincoln accused him of having ambitions to be a dictator. *Who am I?* Joseph Hooker

Name _____

Date _____

The Emancipation Proclamation

President Abraham Lincoln issued this Emancipation Proclamation on September 22, 1862.

That on the 1st day of January, A.D. 1863, all persons held as slaves within any state or designated part of a state the people whereof shall then be in rebellion against the United States shall be then, thenceforward, and forever free; and the executive government of the United States, including the military and naval authority thereof, will recognize and maintain the freedom of such persons.

Directions: Check your understanding by answering these questions.

1. Define *emancipation:* _____

    Define *proclamation:* _____

2. Did Lincoln's proclamation free all the slaves? If not, what slaves did not gain their freedom under the proclamation? _____

    _____

3. How would the proclamation be enforced? _____

    _____

4. Why did Lincoln wait until the fall of 1862 to make emancipation of the slaves part of the war effort? _____

    _____

5. How did Southerners react to the proclamation? _____

    _____

6. How did Northerners react? _____

    _____

Extra Challenge: Find black slaves' descriptions of how they reacted when they heard the news about emancipation. Copy some of these out to create a striking and moving class display.

           Focus on U.S. History:
The Era of the Civil War and Reconstruction

Name _____

Date _____

Graphing the War

Directions: Here are some figures and graphs about the numbers of people involved in the war. Follow the individual directions for each.

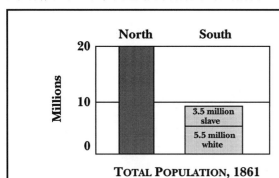

Population Bar Graph Question:

What does this bar graph tell you about the North and the South as the war began? Do you see any advantages or disadvantages for one side or the other from this graph?

Line Graph Questions:

1. Which side had the advantage in numbers of men serving?

2. Did the difference between the two sides stay the same during the course of the war?

3. How does this graph relate to the bar graph above?

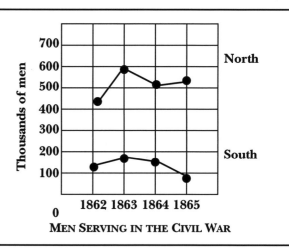

CASUALTIES OF THE CIVIL WAR	North	South
Total Troops	1,566,000	800,000
Wounded	275,000	90,000
Died of Wounds	110,000	94,000
Died of Disease	250,000	164,000

(Numbers are approximate.)

Casualties Chart Directions:

Use the information in this chart to create two pie charts showing the large number of casualties suffered by both sides in the Civil War.

Focus on U.S. History:
The Era of the Civil War and Reconstruction

Time Line of the War

Directions: Continue the time line you began in Unit 1. Add the clashes from Worksheet 7, The Battles, in this unit, plus any other significant battles of the war. Add the events listed below to your time line too. Include a brief description of each. Illustrations would also enhance the time line.

Fort Sumter supply ship turns back.

Lincoln's first inaugural

West Virginia is formed.

Union naval blockade of the South begins.

The *Trent* affair

Confederate draft law

Slavery in Washington, D.C., is abolished.

Slavery is outlawed in the territories.

Lee takes command of Army of Northern Virginia.

Preliminary Emancipation Proclamation

Emancipation Proclamation goes into effect.

Union draft law

Bureau of Colored Troops is established.

New York City draft riots

Gettysburg Address

Grant takes command of all Union armies.

Lincoln is reelected.

U.S. Congress approves Thirteenth Amendment.

Lincoln's second inaugural

Lee surrenders at Appomattox Court House.

Lincoln is assassinated.

Andrew Johnson becomes U.S. president.

Booth is shot and killed.

Union soldiers are sent home.

Thirteenth Amendment is ratified.

Focus on U.S. History:
The Era of the Civil War and Reconstruction

The Gettysburg Address

Abraham Lincoln delivered this speech at the dedication of the Union burial ground at the Gettysburg battlefield. It is one of the great speeches of all time.

Four score and seven years ago our fathers brought forth on this continent a new nation, conceived in Liberty, and dedicated to the proposition that all men are created equal.

Now, we are engaged in a great civil war, testing whether that nation or any nation so conceived and so dedicated, can long endure. We are met on a great battle-field of that war. We have come to dedicate a portion of that field, as a final resting place for those who here gave their lives that that nation might live. It is altogether fitting and proper that we should do this.

But, in a larger sense, we can not dedicate—we can not consecrate—can not hallow—this ground. The brave men, living and dead, who struggled here, have consecrated it, far above our poor power to add or detract. The world will little note, nor long remember, what we say here, but it can never forget what they did here. It is for us the living, rather, to be dedicated here to the unfinished work which they who fought here have thus far so nobly advanced. It is rather for us to be here dedicated to the great task remaining before us—that from these honored dead we take increased devotion to that cause for which they gave the last full measure of devotion—that we here highly resolve that these dead shall not have died in vain—that this nation, under God, shall have a new birth of freedom—and that government of the people, by the people, for the people, shall not perish from the earth.

Directions: Discuss in class what makes this such an effective, memorable speech. What relevance does it have, if any, today?

The *Monitor* and the *Merrimac*

The *Monitor* and the *Merrimac*

Directions: You probably know that the battle between the *Monitor* and the *Merrimac* marked the first use of ironclad ships in warfare. It was an exciting battle! Read this description of it, written by Charles Martin, a navy surgeon who witnessed it. Imagine yourself in the midst of the battle, aboard one of the ships or watching from the shore.

First, the Merrimac attacks wooden warships:

The shot of the starboard battery rattles on the iron roof of the *Merrimac*. She answers with a shell; it sweeps the forward pivot gun, it kills and wounds ten of the gun's crew. A second slaughters the marines at the after pivot gun. . . . She bears down on the *Cumberland*. She rams her just aft the starboard bow. The ram goes into the sides of the ship as a knife goes into a cheese. . . . The battle rages, broadside answers broadside, and the sanded deck is red and slippery with the blood of the wounded and dying. . . .

The *Merrimac* turns to the *Congress*. She is aground, but she fires her guns till the red-hot shot from the enemy sets her on fire, and the flames drive the men away from the battery. She has forty years of seasoning; she burns like a torch. Her commanding officer is killed, and her deck strewn with killed and wounded.

The next day, the Monitor appears:

Sunday morning, March 9th, the *Merrimac* is coming out to finish her work. She will destroy the [grounded] *Minnesota*. As she nears her, the *Monitor* appears from behind the helpless ship; she has slipped in during the night, and so quietly, her presence is unknown in the camp. And David goes out to meet Goliath, and every man who can walk to the beach sits down there, spectators of the first iron-clad battle in the world.

The day is calm, the smoke hangs thick on the water, the low vessels are hidden by the smoke. They are so sure of their invulnerability, they fight at arms' length. They fight so near the shore, the flash of their guns is seen, and the noise is heard of the heavy shot pounding the armor. They haul out for breath, and again disappear in the smoke. The *Merrimac* stops firing, the smoke lifts, she is running down the *Monitor*, but she has left her ram in the *Cumberland*. The *Monitor* slips away, turns, and renews the action.

One P.M.—they have fought since 8:30 A.M. The crews of both ships are suffocating under the armor. The frames supporting the iron roof of the *Merrimac* are sprung and shattered. The turret of the *Monitor* is dented with shot, and is revolved with difficulty. The captain of the *Merrimac* is wounded in the leg; the captain of the *Monitor* is blinded with powder. It is a drawn game. The *Merrimac*, leaking badly, goes back to Norfolk; the *Monitor* returns to Hampton Roads.

Focus on U.S. History:
The Era of the Civil War and Reconstruction

The Personal Face of War

The objective of this unit is to help students to understand the impact of the Civil War on individuals North and South, civilians as well as soldiers. Confederate and Union soldiers fought for various reasons, but their army experiences were similar, at least for whites. African-Americans were barred from serving in the Union army at first; when finally allowed, they distinguished themselves on the battlefield. Black slaves continued to labor as before—until the Union army came to their locale and they flocked to Union lines. Women's lives were greatly affected by the war, as wives took over their husbands' business and farming operations, and other women worked in wartime factories, collected supplies for soldiers, or served as nurses. In the North, the wartime economy hummed along, but some civil liberties were reined in. Increasingly, the war caused great hardship in the agricultural South, as homes, crops, and machinery were destroyed and livestock and personal property were carried off. Manufactured goods were in short supply, and inflation soared. This unit's activities draw students into a greater understanding of these personal aspects of the war.

Student Activities

Civil War Songs introduces two of the most popular Civil War songs, one of the Confederacy and one of the Union. Questions guide students in interpreting the lyrics. For an extra challenge, students find the rest of the lyrics and the melodies for these songs and give a class rendition of them, much as Civil War soldiers might have done.

The Life of a Soldier is two firsthand accounts of the difficulties and dangers of being a soldier. Students then find and read a diary, memoir, or series of letters written by a Civil War soldier and write a short story about that soldier's war experiences. (See the worksheet for detailed directions for this activity.)

Southern Women in Wartime recounts two southern women's experiences dealing with wartime disruption of their accustomed way of life. Students continue by finding and reading more southern women's diaries and memoirs and then writing a series of diary entries describing how one of them might have coped with the sudden and often radical change in her way of life.

Northern Women in Wartime presents photographs of northern women who contributed greatly to caring for sick and wounded soldiers during the war. Students identify Clara Barton and Dorothea Dix and describe the contributions of these two women and of the U.S. Sanitary Commission during the war. The Answer Key provides suggestions for ways to extend this activity.

Black Slaves During the War is excerpts from wartime memoirs with contrasting descriptions of black slaves during the war. Students consider why slaves might have continued working on plantations during the war and whether it was unusual for slaves to depart as soon as Union troops arrived.

A Batch of Deserters reproduces an ad from an 1863 newspaper for four deserters, with individual descriptions. Students imagine themselves to be one of the men and write a first-person narrative about the experiences that led him to desert.

Wartime Destruction shows two photographs of burned-out wartime buildings, one from the U.S. South during the Civil War, the other from Sarajevo, in the former Yugoslavia. Students discuss what they think they are seeing and then go on to consider the definition of civil war and its effects on civilian and military populations through history, finishing with a comparison of the U.S. and Yugoslavian civil wars.

Black Soldiers—Yes or No? presents excerpts from congressional debate about allowing African-Americans to enlist as soldiers in the Union army. Guided by interpretive questions, students identify the points each side made in the debate.

Wartime Medical Care uses a soldier's description of wounded men trying to retreat to get medical help after the battle of Shiloh, along with a photograph of a Civil War surgeon's tools. This will start students on an investigation of Civil War medical care that could culminate in a classroom display.

The Peace Democrats introduces students to the views of the numerous Peace Democrats of the North through the words of their most outspoken member, Clement Vallandigham. Students explain how the Gettysburg Address answers one of Vallandigham's points; then they role-play a debate between supporters of Vallandigham's views and supporters of Seward's "irrepressible conflict" and Lincoln's "part slave and part free" positions from the final activity in Unit 1.

In **Why Enlist?** a white Union, an African-American Union, and a white Confederate soldier explain in their own words why they enlisted. Students then role-play a discussion among Civil War soldiers on why they enlisted.

Civil Liberties in Wartime presents the views of Abraham Lincoln and ex-president Franklin Pierce on suppression of civil liberties during the war. Students investigate the arrest of Congressman Vallandigham for antiwar speeches and then apply the Lincoln or Pierce views to write an editorial about the arrest.

Becoming Free presents ex-slaves' descriptions of the moment that they became free. Students then try to imagine how that might have felt and describe their emotions and reactions.

The Personal Face of War

The Civil War had an enormous impact on the entire nation. It reached into the lives of civilians as well as soldiers.

The Soldiers

Most southern soldiers felt they were fighting for their homeland. In their view, they were defending their individual states and the South as a whole from an aggressive North that wanted to destroy and their way of life.

Most northern soldiers fought to keep the Union together. Whites and blacks also enlisted for the pay. Many African-Americans also fought for freedom, once they were allowed to enlist and fight. After President Lincoln issued the Emancipation Proclamation, putting an end to slavery also became a goal of the Union army—but not necessarily of most white soldiers.

> Union and Confederate pickets (soldiers guarding the edges of their army's camp) often got together on neutral ground to trade for items like tobacco, coffee, and sugar.

In March 1863, Congress passed a conscription (draft) act. Laborers in northern cities erupted into riots. They were angry at being required to fight to free blacks who would, they thought, flood to the North and take away their jobs.

Women in Wartime

Women were not allowed to serve as soldiers in the Civil War era. But quite a few did, disguised as men. Their secret was often discovered when they were treated for wounds.

Equally daring were the Union and Confederate female spies—for example, teenagers Belle Boyd and Nancy Hart.

As in the Revolutionary War, this conflict opened new doors for women in both North and South. Many worked as army nurses. Others labored in ammunition plants and other war-related industries. Volunteers for the U.S. Sanitary Commission collected materials the soldiers needed.

> Dr. Mary Edwards Walker and Sally Tomkins, a nurse, held commissions in the Union and Confederate armies, respectively.

Women also ran farms and businesses and filled government posts while the men were away fighting.

Confederate cadet in marching outfit

Private in the 7th Regiment, New York

(continued)

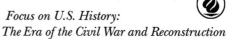

The Personal Face of War (continued)

Life in the Wartime North

The northern economy thrived on the war. Its factories churned out the vast supplies the army needed. However, taxes and prices were high, feeding workers' resentment and strikes.

> In 1863, soldiers arrested Congressman Clement Vallandigham, of Ohio, a Peace Democrat (or Copperhead) for his strong antiwar statements. He was merely exiled to the Confederacy and returned in 1864 to campaign against Lincoln.

Congress and President Lincoln restricted some civil rights. In certain areas of the country, Lincoln suspended the *writ of habeas corpus*, which normally protects U.S. citizens from being arrested and held in jail without a trial. Lincoln ordered the U.S. army to arrest people who spoke out strongly against the military draft or the war itself. Many people were in fact arrested and held, but the policy wasn't harshly enforced.

Life in the Wartime South

As the war dragged on, civilians in the South had an increasingly hard time of it. The Union's naval blockade created shortages of all sorts of goods. Confederate presses turned out sheaves of paper money, which caused disastrous inflation. Resentment of the draft, and its exemptions, grew steadily.

Worst off were civilians caught in the path of battle. They saw their homes and crops destroyed, their livestock and personal property carried off. Women and children found themselves with no shelter, money, or food.

Carolina home

Focus on U.S. History:
The Era of the Civil War and Reconstruction

Civil War Songs

The songs that soldiers and civilians on each side of the war sang reflected their feelings and loyalties. Here are lyrics from two of the most popular Civil War songs.

WE ARE COMING	THE BONNIE BLUE FLAG
We are coming, Father Abraham,	We are a band of brothers,
Three hundred thousand more,	And natives to the soil,
From Mississippi's winding stream	Fighting for the property
And from New England's shore.	We gained by honest toil.
We leave our ploughs and workshops,	And when our rights were threatened,
Our wives and children dear,	The cry rose near and far:
With hearts too full for utterance,	Hurrah for the bonnie blue flag
With but a silent tear;	That bears a single star!
We dare not look behind us,	*Chorus*
But steadfastly before:	Hurrah! Hurrah!
We are coming, Father Abraham,	For the bonnie blue flag
Three hundred thousand more.	That bears a single star.

Directions: Answer these questions about the lyrics.

1. Which side in the conflict would have sung "We Are Coming"? _____

   Which side would have sung "The Bonnie Blue Flag"? _____

2. What inspired the lyrics of "We Are Coming"? Who is Father Abraham? Who are the "three hundred thousand more"? _____

   _____

3. What is "The Bonnie Blue Flag" referring to when it says "our rights were threatened"?

   _____

4. Is "The Bonnie Blue Flag" accurate when it says these soldiers are "fighting for the property we gained by honest toil"? _____

Extra Challenge: Find the rest of the lyrics and the melodies for these two songs. With classmates, give a spirited rendition of one of them, as if you were Civil War soldiers singing to boost your spirits.

The Life of a Soldier

North or South, the life of the soldier during the war was a trial. Read these soldiers' accounts.

On the March—Major Wilder Dwight

Our path was a rough one, through a river, over rocks, and through deep mud, on, on, on. . . . The day was long and hot; the artillery labored over the almost impassable road. . . . Tired and footsore, we lay down to sleep in the woods. Marching for eighteen hours, and such marching! the bivouac, in the warm, pleasant night is a luxury. The next morning we start again, and ford the Shenandoah [which is] swift, and up to one's middle. Fording is an exciting, amusing, long task. . . . Our tents and baggage are all sixteen miles back. . . .

It is late Friday evening before we get bivouacked. Many of the men are barefoot and without rations. Saturday morning it begins early to rain, and ever since we have been dripping under this easterly storm. . . . I wish you could look at our regiment under rude shelters of rails and straw, and dripping in this cold storm. . . .

Rain! rain! rain! March! march! march! What a life! We marched fifteen miles yesterday, in mud and rain.

On the Firing Line—Corporal James Hosmer

We were now only screened from the rebel works by a thin hedge. Here the rifle-balls began to cut keen and sharp through the air about us; and the cannonade, as the east now began to redden, reached its height,—a continual deafening uproar, hurling the air against one in great waves, till it felt almost like a wall of rubber, bounding and rebounding from the body . . . and, through all, the bursting of the shells within the rebel lines, and the keen, deadly whistle of well-aimed bullets. . . . I believe I felt no sensation of fear, nor do I think those about me did. . . .

It is out of the question to advance here in line of battle; it seems almost out of the question to advance in any order: but the word is given, "Forward!" and on we go. Know that this whole space is swept by a constant patter of balls: it is really a "leaden rain." We go crawling and stooping: but now and then before us rises in plain view the line of earthworks, smoky with volleys; while all about us fall the balls, now sending a lot of little splinters from a stump, now knocking the dead wood out of the old tree-trunk that is sheltering me, now driving up a cloud of dust from a little knoll, or cutting off the head of a weed just under my hand as with an invisible knife.

(continued)

The Life of a Soldier *(continued)*

Part 1 Directions: Find and read a Civil War diary, memoir, or series of letters, perhaps by a soldier from your locality who served in the war. Most libraries have some personal accounts of Civil War experiences. Also, Civil War sites on the Internet can direct you to on-line diaries, letters, and memoirs. Record below at least five Internet sites with personal Civil War accounts. List a mix of northern and southern accounts.

Civil War Accounts at Library (include call number/letters, title, and author):

Internet/World Wide Web Sites with Civil War Accounts (include site name and address, and name and home state of person who is telling his or her Civil War story):

Part 2 Directions: Now write a short story about the experience of one of the people whose Civil War account you have read. Or, write a series of diary entries or letters home telling your loved ones about your own Civil War experiences.

Civil War-era diary, badge, and tobacco tin

Focus on U.S. History:
The Era of the Civil War and Reconstruction

Southern Women in Wartime

Southern women on large farms and plantations during the war faced enormous challenges, especially when the war reached their own land. Here's a soldier's eyewitness account of the sudden change of fortune of a Mrs. Ramsay.

> When the war commenced, the owner of this magnificent estate enlisted in the army and was made a colonel of cavalry. He fell in a cavalry engagement on the Rapahannock, leaving a wife and three young children. The advance of the army, its sudden appearance, left Mrs. Ramsay no time to remove her personal estate, or to send her Negroes to Richmond for safekeeping. Fitz-Hugh Lee disputed Sheridan's advance. The fighting began on this estate. Charges by squadrons and regiments were made through the corn fields. Horses, cattle, hogs, sheep, were seized by the cavalrymen. The garden, filled with young vegetables, was spoiled. In an hour there was complete desolation. The hundred Negroes—cook, steward, chambermaid, house and field hands, old and young—all left their work and followed the army. Mrs. Ramsay was left to do her own work. The parlors of the stately mansion were taken over by the surgeons for a hospital. The change which Mrs. Ramsay experienced was from affluence to abject poverty, from power to sudden helplessness.

Southern women coped with these difficulties. Here's an excerpt from the memoirs of Victoria Clayton of Alabama.

> We were blockaded on every side, could get nothing from without, so had to make everything at home . . . it became necessary for every home to be supplied with spinning wheels and the old-fashioned loom, in order to manufacture clothing for the members of the family. . . .
> We made good crops every year, but after the second year we planted provision crops entirely, except enough cotton for home use. . . . My duties were numerous and often laborious.

Directions: Read some more diaries and memoirs written by southern women who ran their farms during the war. Then write a series of diary entries for Mrs. Ramsay describing how she coped with her sudden change of lifestyle.

Northern Women in Wartime

Directions: Like southern women, northern women worked their farms while their husbands, brothers, and sons were away at war. Like southern women, northern women also worked to help their soldiers. Learn more about this by answering the questions about the pictures below.

Who is the woman to the left? Describe her contribution to the northern war effort.

_____

_____

_____

_____

_____

Who is the woman to the right? Describe her contribution to the northern war effort.

_____

_____

_____

_____

The woman in the photo on the left helped organize the U.S. Sanitary Commission. Describe what kinds of work the commission did.

_____

_____

_____

_____

Black Slaves During the War

Read these descriptions of black slaves in the South during the Civil War.

Memoir excerpt—Victoria Clayton of Alabama (whose husband was away at war)

There was no white person on the plantation beside myself and children. . . . I entrusted the planting and cultivation of the various crops to old Joe. He had been my husband's nurse in infancy, and we always loved and trusted him. . . . Each night, when the day's work was done, Joe came in to make a report of everything that had been done on the plantation that day.

With nearly every white man of proper age and health enlisted in the army, with the country filled with white women, children, and old, infirm men, with thousands of slaves to be controlled and caused through their labor to feed and clothe the people at home and to provide for our army—I often wonder, as I contemplate those bygone days of labor and sorrow, and recall how peacefully we moved on and accomplished what we did.

Memoir excerpt—Charles C. Coffin, war correspondent

Passing by one of the Negro cabins on the estate [after the Union army arrived], I saw a middle-aged colored woman packing a bundle [preparing to follow the Union army]. . . .

"Do you think it right, auntie, to leave your mistress, who has taken care of you so long?"

She had been busy with her bundle, but stopped now and stood erect before me, her hands on her hips. Her black eyes flashed.

"Taken care of me! What did she ever do for me? Haven't I been her cook for more than thirty years? Haven't I cooked every meal she ever ate in that house? What has she done for me in return? She has sold my children down South, one after another. She has whipped me when I cried for them. She has treated me like a hog, sir! Yes, sir, like a hog!"

Directions: Consider these questions in a small group or class discussion.

1. Why did slaves stay in place on plantations, laboring, when there were few or no white men around to force them to stay?

2. When the Union army arrived, how common were reactions like the middle-aged black woman's?

Focus on U.S. History:
The Era of the Civil War and Reconstruction

A Batch of Deserters

During the war, many soldiers *deserted*—left the army without permission, with no intention of returning. Here's an 1863 newspaper ad for a group of deserters.

DESERTERS!

THE FOLLOWING NAMED SOLDIERS, enlisted for Old Regiments, have deserted from Camp McClellan Davenport, Iowa:

Albert Prince, born in Frederick county, Maryland; 21 years old; farmer by occupation; enlisted September 9th, 1862, at Kyokuk, by Major Wm. H. Belknap, for three years; has grey eyes, brown hair, and fair complexion; 5 feet 8 inches high. 15th Iowa infantry.

J.L. Braden, born in Decatur county, Indiana; aged 23 years; by occupation a farmer; enlisted at Davenport, Iowa, Aug. 16; has hazel eyes, black hair and dark complexion; height, 5 feet 10 inches.

William B. Jones, born in Orange county, New York; aged 24 years; by occupation a carpenter; enlisted at Iowa City, Iowa, July 31; has black eyes, sandy hair and dark complexion; height 5 feet 5 inches.

John Houghton, born in Hardin county, Ohio; aged 19 years; by occupation a farmer; enlisted at Davenport Iowa, Sept. 20th; has grey eyes, light hair and light complexion; height, 5 feet $6\frac{1}{2}$ inches.

Any one apprehending any one or all of said soldiers, will be paid all reasonable cost of tranportation and subsistence, together with a reward of five dollars, when said deserters are returned to the Commanding Officer of Camp McClellan.

R. M. LITTLER,

Capt. 2d Iowa Inft., Com'dg Camp McClellan, Davenport, Oct 4, 1862.   dtf.

Directions: Imagine you are one of these soldiers. Write a first-person narrative about your experiences—your personal and family background, why you enlisted in the army, what life in the army was like, why you deserted or left for a while, how things turned out for you.

Wartime Destruction

Directions: Study the two photographs below. Then discuss in class when you think each photograph may have been taken and what each one shows. Your teacher will tell you how to complete the rest of this activity.

Black Soldiers—Yes or No?

In January 1863, Congress considered a bill to enlist 150,000 black soldiers. This was a controversial issue. Here are some excerpts from the congressional debate.

John J. Crittenden, representative from Kentucky

This plan of bringing black men into your military service will prove an act of cruelty to the slaves, but of profit to no one. Can they sympathize with us in the motives that actuate us in carrying on this war? That Constitution for which we are fighting makes them slaves; and yet you now call upon them to assist you in restoring its supremacy. . . .

For every black soldier you may muster into the service, you will disarm more brave soldiers who will think you have degraded them by this sort of military association. You cannot carry into the field, I repeat, an army made up of the African race. The slave is not a soldier, and he cannot be a soldier. It is not in the nature of things.

John J. Crittendon

Thaddeus Stevens, representative from Pennsylvania

Sickness, the sword, and absenteeism have taken half our troops; and in four months one-fourth more will be taken by the expiration of their time. How are you to supply their place except by colored soldiers?

But suppose we could recruit our armies by white volunteers, is that any argument against employing blacks? Why should our race be exposed to suffering and disease when the African might endure his equal share of it? Is it wise, is it humane, to send your kindred to battle and to death, when you might put the colored man in the ranks and let him bear a part of the conflict between the rebel and his enfranchised slave?

But it is said that our soldiers would object to [blacks'] employment in arms. It would be a strange taste that would prefer themselves to face the death-bearing heights of Fredericksburg, and be buried in trenches at the foot of them, than to see it done by colored soldiers. I do not believe it. . . .

But we are not fighting for the freedom of the slaves; we are fighting for the life of the nation; and, if in the heat of such strife the chains of the bondman are melted off, I shall thank God all the more. . . .

I ask, when did any civilized nation refuse to use their slaves in the defense of their country when . . . required? Never! All have used them, and uniformly given them their freedom for their services.

(continued)

Black Soldiers—Yes or No? *(continued)*

Samuel O. Cox, representative from Ohio

The Confederate States will not treat our black soldiers as the equals of their white soldiers or of our white soldiers; and the result will be . . . that they will, if captured, receive none of the advantages of the laws of war, but all the terrible consequences of being outlawed from the international code—slavery, imprisonment, and perhaps death. And how, sir, can we retaliate for any such injuries or outrages? . . . No genuine friend of the Negro would try to persuade him to take the position of a soldier in our army, knowing how the Confederate Government has determined to treat Negro soldiers.

Directions: Use what you have read to answer the following questions.

1. How might the fact that Crittenden was from Kentucky affect his stand on the use of

   black soldiers? _____

   _____

2. What political party did Cox probably belong to? _____

   What political party did Stevens probably belong to? _____

3. List the various reasons opponents gave for *not* using black soldiers: _____

   _____

   _____

4. List the various reasons Stevens gave for using black soldiers: _____

   _____

   _____

5. Does Stevens sound respectful of blacks? Why did he make his argument this way?

   _____

   _____

How did black soldiers perform in the Civil War? As you might expect! Once blacks were allowed into combat, battle reports routinely commented, "The colored troops fought bravely." Dr. Seth Rogers, an army surgeon who treated blacks after battle, commented in his notes, "Braver men never lived."

---

66   *Focus on U.S. History:*
The Era of the Civil War and Reconstruction

Wartime Medical Care

The casualty rate in the Civil War was very high. Here's one soldier's description of the aftermath of the battle of Shiloh.

Lieutenant William Stevenson (1862)

In this ride of twelve miles alongside of the routed army, I saw more of human agony and woe than I trust I will ever again be called on to witness. The retreating host wound along a narrow and almost impassable road, extending some seven or eight miles in length. Here was a long line of wagons loaded with wounded, piled in like bags of grain, groaning and cursing, while the mules plunged on in mud and water belly-deep, the water sometimes coming into the wagons. Next came a straggling regiment of infantry pressing on past the train of wagons, then a stretcher borne upon the shoulders of four men, carrying a wounded officer, then soldiers staggering along, with an arm broken and hanging down, or other fearful wounds which were enough to destroy life.

A cold, drizzling rain commenced about nightfall, and soon came harder and faster, then turned to pitiless blind hail. This storm raged with unrelenting violence for three hours. I passed long wagon trains with wounded and dying soldiers, without even a blanket to shield them from the driving sleet and hail, which fell in stones as large as partridge eggs, until it lay on the ground two inches deep.

Some three hundred men died during that awful retreat, and their bodies were thrown out to make room for others who, although wounded, had struggled on through the storm, hoping to find shelter, rest, and medical care.

Surgeon's kit

Surgical pliers

Directions: What kind of medical treatment could those wounded Shiloh soldiers expect once they reached a field hospital? What would a Civil War doctor use the instruments shown above for? Research to find answers to these questions. You could then create a classroom display of Civil War photographs that illustrate the topic of this activity sheet, Civil War Medical Care.

The Peace Democrats

Many northern Democrats opposed the war. Clement Vallandigham was the most outspoken of them. He summarized his views in a speech to Congress in 1863.

Clement L. Vallandigham, congressman from Ohio

Sir, twenty months have elapsed, but the rebellion is not crushed out; its military power has not been broken; the insurgents have not dispersed. The Union is not restored; nor the Constitution maintained; nor the laws enforced. A thousand millions have been expended and three hundred thousand lives lost or bodies mangled; and today the Confederate flag is still near the Potomac and the Ohio, and the Confederate government stronger, many times, than at the beginning.

You have utterly, signally, disastrously—I will not say ignominiously—failed to subdue ten millions of "rebels".... [A]ll the persistent and stupendous efforts of the most gigantic warfare of modern times have, through your incompetency and folly, availed nothing to crush them out, cut off though they have been by your blockade from all the

Clement L. Vallandigham

world, and dependent only upon their own courage and resources.... You have not conquered the South. You never will.... But money you have expended without limit, and blood poured out like water. Defeat, debt, taxation, sepulchres, these are your trophies. In vain the people gave you treasure and the soldier yielded up his life.... The war for the Union is, in your hands, a most bloody and costly failure.

On union and disunion:

Is there an "irrepressible conflict" between the slaveholding and non-slaveholding states? If so, then there is an end of all union and forever.... And if "this Union cannot endure part slave and part free," then it is already and finally dissolved.

But I deny this doctrine.... Sir, the fundamental idea of the Constitution is the perfect and eternal compatibility of a union of states "part slave and part free"; else the Constitution never would have been framed, nor the Union founded; and seventy years of successful experiment have approved the wisdom of the plan.... The sole question today is between the Union with slavery, or final disunion, and, I think, anarchy and despotism.

Directions:

1. Explain how the Gettysburg Address is an effective answer to the first part of Vallandigham's speech.

2. Role-play a debate between supporters of Vallandigham's views on union and disunion, and supporters of Lincoln's "part slave and part free," and Seward's "irrepressible conflict" positions from Unit 1.

Why Enlist?

Did men enlist in the Civil War because of patriotism, or because they were against slavery, or . . .? Here is how a few soldiers answered that question.

John W. Haley, private from Maine (1862)

During the summer of 1862 the North at last removed its gloves and a call was issued for 600,000 troops. . . . Our enlisting was like many other things in this world: one started and the rest thoughtlessly followed, like sheep over a fence, until six of us had enlisted from one class in Sunday School. Speaking for myself, I had *no* inclination for the business, but once committed in a momentary spasm of enthusiasm to serve under certain circumstances, which I never expected to occur, I found myself face to face with the alternative of going or showing a white liver by backing out. I decided to do as I had agreed and enlisted for "three years, unless sooner discharged." *Shot* or *starved* should have been added to the contract.*

Prince Lambkin, former slave (1862)

Our masters, they have lived under the flag [of the United States], they got their wealth under it, and everything beautiful for their children. Under it they have ground us up, and put us in their pocket for money. But the first minute they think that ole flag means freedom for us colored people, they pull it right down and run up the rag of their own. But we'll never desert the ole flag, boys, never: we have lived under it for many years, and we'll die for it now.

Randolph H. McKim, lieutenant from Maryland (1861)

Day after day the spirit of the epoch wrought in me more and more mightily till I felt that I could no longer resist the call to follow the example of my kindred, my friends, and my fellow students, and enlist in the southern Army. . . . By this time, the cause of the South had become identified with liberty itself, and, being of military age, I felt myself bound by every high and holy consideration to take up arms to deliver Maryland from the invaders who were polluting her soil [the Union army].

Directions: Role-play a discussion among Civil War soldiers from both sides on their motives for enlisting in the war.

* From *The Rebel Yell & the Yankee Hurrah: The Civil War Journal of a Maine Volunteer,* Ruth L. Silliker, ed. (Camden, ME: Down East Books, 1985).

Civil Liberties in Wartime

The U.S. Constitution allows the president to suspend the *writ of habeus corpus* in times of rebellion. Without habeus corpus, people can be held in jail without trial. President Lincoln used this constitutional power during the Civil War and allowed the military arrest of Congressman Vallandigham for antiwar speeches. Here's what Lincoln and his opponents had to say about the suppression of civil liberties during the war.

Abraham Lincoln (1863)

Mr. Vallandigham's arrest was made because he was laboring, with some effect, to prevent the raising of troops, to encourage desertions from the army, and to leave the rebellion without an adequate military force to suppress it. . . . Must I shoot a simple-minded soldier boy who deserts, while I must not touch a hair of a wily agitator who induces him to desert?

I can no more be persuaded that the government can constitutionally take no strong measures in time of rebellion, because it can be shown that the same could not be lawfully taken in time of peace, than I can be persuaded that a particular drug is not good medicine for a sick man because it can be shown not to be good food for a well one. Nor am I able to appreciate the [supposed] danger . . . that the American people will by means of military arrests during the rebellion lose the right of public discussion, the liberty of speech and the press, the law of evidence, trial by jury, and *habeas corpus* throughout the indefinite peaceful future . . . any more than I am able to believe that a man could contract so strong an appetite for emetics [agents that cause vomiting] curing temporary illness as to persist in feeding upon them during the remainder of his healthful life.

Ex-President Franklin Pierce (1863)

We only ask that you shall give to us that which you claim for yourselves, and that which every freeman, and every man who respects himself, will have—freedom of speech, the right to exercise all the franchises conferred by the Constitution upon American citizens. Can you safely deny us these? Will you not trample upon your own rights if you refuse to listen? Do you not create revolution when you say that our persons may be rightfully seized, our property confiscated, our homes entered? . . . Remember this, that the bloody, and treasonable, and revolutionary doctrine of public necessity can be proclaimed by a mob as well as by a government.

Franklin Pierce

Directions: Read more about the details of the Vallandigham case. Then write a newspaper editorial supporting or condemning the congressman's arrest.

Becoming Free

How did it feel to be instantly transformed from slave to free person? Here's how some ex-slaves described that moment.

The end of the war came like that—like you snap your fingers. Everyone was singing. We was all walking on golden clouds. Hallelujah!

Everybody went wild. We all felt like heroes, and like nobody had made us that way but ourselves. We was free! Just like that, we was free.—Felix Haywood

---

When the Yankee soldiers came, the blacks ran and hid under the beds, and the soldiers came and poked their bayonets under the beds and shouted, "Come on out from under there. You're free."—Dicey Thomas

---

I remember well how the roads was full of folks walking and walking along, when the blacks were freed. Didn't know where they was going. Just going to see about something else, somewhere else. Meet a body in the road and they ask, "Where you going?" "Don't know." "What you going to do?" "Don't know."—Robert Falls

---

We had no time for any celebration, for [our former master] made us get right off the place—just like you take an old horse and turn it loose. You see a lot of cattle in the field eating the grass with a fence 'round them, and then somebody opens the gate an' says, "Git!" That's how we was. No money, no nothin'—just turned loose without nothin'.—William Matthews

---

I guess we musta celebrated Emancipation about twelve times. Every time a bunch of northern soldiers would come through, they would tell us we was free, and we'd begin celebratin'.—Ambrose Douglass

---

Directions: Try to imagine what it might have felt like to become free suddenly. Describe your emotions and reactions.

Reconstruction

The objective of this unit is to help students better understand Reconstruction—its programs, the political controversy it created, Reconstruction's successes and failures, and why it ended. After the Civil War, plans were needed to restore order to the South, to help recently freed slaves develop independent lives, and to bring the former Confederate states back into the Union. This process of Reconstruction lasted from 1865 to 1877. Under the moderate Reconstruction policies of President Lincoln and his successor, Andrew Johnson, southern states formed new governments and elected congressmen, while the Freedmen's Bureau helped freed slaves get an education and sign labor contracts. Sharecropping emerged as the new postwar farm labor system. But the southern states began passing "black codes" that severely limited African-Americans' rights. Radical Republicans got control of Congress and took charge of Reconstruction. They wrote the Fourteenth and Fifteenth Amendments, put the southern states under martial law, made sure blacks could vote and hold office, and nearly removed President Johnson from office because of his more moderate views. White Southerners seethed under northern military and political rule and gradually regained control, once again restricting blacks' rights. Finally, Northerners gave up and ended Reconstruction with the Compromise of 1877. This unit's activities will give students a better grasp of these various aspects of Reconstruction.

Student Activities

The South, Before and After provides students with a framework for identifying aspects of southern life that were different before and after the war.

Plans for Reconstruction is a chart that students complete to differentiate the various Reconstruction plans.

In **Freedom's Choices**, after reading ex-slaves' descriptions of their postwar prospects and choices, students role-play a black family discussing what they will do now that they are free.

Reconstruction and You has students put themselves into the place of various individuals during Reconstruction and then describe their role in Reconstruction, how it affects them, and what they think of it.

The Reconstruction Amendments presents Section 1 of the Thirteenth, Fourteenth, and Fifteenth Amendments to the U.S. Constitution. Students answer interpretive questions to understand more about these important amendments. The Extra Challenge asks students to find current applications of the due process and equal protection clauses.

Black Codes is excerpts from some southern laws of the 1860's restricting blacks' civil rights, followed by a series of scenarios. Students decide whether the scenarios violate one of the codes and, if so, which provision of the code in question.

White Southerners and Reconstruction presents an 1866 report by Major General Carl Schurz, an emissary of President Johnson, on white attitudes in the postwar South. Students write an 1870's follow-up report detailing how the Reconstruction problems Schurz predicted because of white Southerners' attitudes and preconceptions became reality.

Impeachment—Yes or No? presents the charges brought against President Johnson in impeachment proceedings in the U.S. Congress; students evaluate their validity, guided by focused questions. The Extra Challenge asks students to describe the likely impact on U.S. government had President Johnson been found guilty and removed from office.

Women and the Vote presents the objections of suffragist and abolitionist Elizabeth Cady Stanton to the Fourteenth and Fifteenth Amendments. From this, students summarize the reasons why women's rights advocates were opposed to these amendments.

Black Leaders of Reconstruction asks students to match names of black leaders with their descriptions. For an extra challenge, students can explain why only one woman appears on this list.

The Ku Klux Klan presents some black people's firsthand memories of Klan terror in the Reconstruction South. From this, students role-play a discussion among black family members about various strategies for keeping themselves safe from the Klan.

Slavery vs. Freedom presents photographs of black rural life in Reconstruction times. Students are likely to conclude from the display that living conditions for blacks were little different in freedom or in slavery. Students write an essay discussing how and to what degree life for blacks at the end of Reconstruction was different from their life in slavery.

The Compromise of 1877 focuses on voting records from the 1876 presidential election. Interpretive questions guide students to understand the election's outcome. For an extra challenge, students assume the viewpoint of an African-American former slave, a southern political leader, and a northern Republican, evaluate the Compromise of 1877 from each perspective, and suggest alternatives for those whom it displeased.

In **Reconstruction Time Line** students update their time line from Units 1 and 2.

Reconstruction

The Civil War left the South in ruins.

- Roads, bridges, buildings, and machinery were destroyed.
- Once-rich farm fields were barren or weed choked.
- Confederate money was worthless.
- Farmers and planters had no money or credit to buy seeds and tools so they could start growing crops again.
- The vast labor pool of slaves had dried up.

How could the South restore order so it could rebuild? How were the former slaves supposed to earn a living in this new era of freedom? And how were North and South going to reunite?

Reconstruction Policies

Plans to bring the former Confederate states back into the Union were called **Reconstruction**. This process lasted from 1865 to 1877.

The Republican party, which controlled Congress, was split between Moderates (like President Lincoln) and Radicals (like Congressman Thaddeus Stevens). Moderates favored easy terms for readmitting the southern states. Radicals wanted much tougher terms. They also wanted to weaken the South's planter class and remake southern society along northern lines.

Lincoln might have won out in the end. But John Wilkes Booth assassinated him on April 14, 1865, in Ford's Theatre. The new president, Andrew Johnson, followed a Reconstruction policy almost as moderate as Lincoln's. Lincoln knew how to negotiate and compromise. But Johnson was devilishly stubborn. He locked horns with the Radicals and lost.

President Andrew Johnson

Presidential Reconstruction

The first phase of Reconstruction, directed by President Johnson, followed moderate lines. Southern states formed new governments and elected congressmen. They ratified the Thirteenth Amendment, which banned slavery.

Sharecropping was the South's new postwar system of farm labor. Blacks farmed a plot for a landowner. They lived on credit until the crop came in. Then they got a share of the crop. But it often didn't cover the amount the black farm family owed. Still in debt, the family had no choice but to keep on working for that landowner. One thing about this system that blacks liked, though, was that they directed their own work and lives, even though they remained landless.

(continued)

Focus on U.S. History:
The Era of the Civil War and Reconstruction

Reconstruction (continued)

Former African-American slaves redirected their lives. The Freedmen's Bureau, established by Congress, gave out food to the needy, both black and white. It set up black schools and helped African-Americans find jobs and sign labor contracts. Federal troops protected blacks in the cities.

Many white Southerners, however, wanted nothing to do with fair treatment of African-Americans. The southern states began passing laws called "black codes" that kept the spirit of slavery alive. The black codes put many restrictions on blacks' freedoms—for instance, they required a black to get his employer's permission to leave the farm where he worked. Race riots broke out in cities like Memphis and New Orleans. The Ku Klux Klan emerged and began terrorizing and killing blacks.

Ku Klux Klan terrorizing a family at home

The Radicals Take Charge

Many people in the North wanted the rights of blacks in the South protected. Radical Republicans wrote the Fourteenth Amendment to the U.S. Constitution to do just that. This amendment says that no state can take away

anyone's rights or deny them equal protection of the laws.

During 1866, the Radical Republicans discovered they had enough votes to override any vetoes by President Johnson. Congress now took charge of Reconstruction. The southern states were put under military rule. They had to form new governments and ratify the Fourteenth Amendment.

The southern states also had to allow blacks to vote. Federal soldiers made sure this actually happened. With blacks now voting, many African-Americans were elected to office—local, state, and national. The U.S. Senate saw its first black members, Blanche Bruce and Hiram Revels.

During this period of congressional, or Radical, Reconstruction, many Northerners came South. Most wanted to help blacks get their new lives established and secure equal rights. Some, though, came to make money. Southerners called all these Northerners *carpetbaggers* and resented their presence. Southerners who cooperated with Reconstruction were called *scalawags*.

Impeachment

The struggle between President Johnson and the radicals in control of Congress came to a head in February and March of 1868. Johnson had dismissed Secretary of War Edwin Stanton. This violated the Tenure of Office Act. The House of Representatives used this as an excuse to *impeach* Johnson—charge him with misconduct. The Senate tried him on the charge. If found guilty, Johnson would be removed from office.

The Senate vote was one shy of a guilty verdict.

(continued)

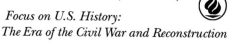

Reconstruction *(continued)*

The Fifteenth Amendment

Radical Republicans had one more goal to achieve. They wanted to be sure black Southerners could vote—partly out of a concern for equal rights, partly because these new voters would support the Republican party. The Fifteenth Amendment, passed by Congress in 1869 and ratified by the states in 1870, gave this guarantee.

Reconstruction Ends

Reconstruction had its successes. Black (and white) lawmakers spent money on schools and roads. Former slaves got educations and found ways to earn a living. New governments

and federal troops restored order. The economy was reborn.

However, white Southerners continued to resist Reconstruction. Their old leaders began to take control again. They found ways to get around the Fifteenth Amendment. They used sharecropping to keep blacks in near-slavery. They restricted many blacks' rights and made rules about keeping whites and blacks separate in public places. Terrorist groups like the Ku Klux Klan flourished.

All this resistance to Reconstruction finally made the Northerners give up. They were tired of worrying about problems in the South. The 1876 presidential election hinged on some disputed votes. The two political parties compromised.

Democrats:	**Republicans:**
Gave the disputed votes to Republican Rutherford B. Hayes.	Agreed to pull all federal troops out of the South.

This agreement was called the Compromise of 1877. With it, Reconstruction was over.

Freedmen's Bureau School in Vicksburg, Mississippi

The South, Before and After

Directions: After the Civil War, living conditions in the South were radically different from the prewar years. Describe prewar and postwar aspects of southern life below. Then, personalize the information. Imagine you are a Southerner of the Civil War era. Describe how your life in 1866 is different from your life before the war.

Prewar	Aspects of southern life	Postwar
	family life	
	farms and plantations	
	farm workers/labor force	
	credit and money supply	
	commerce	
	housing	
	infrastructure (roads, railroads, bridges, levees)	

Focus on U.S. History:
The Era of the Civil War and Reconstruction

Plans for Reconstruction

Directions: Different political leaders and parties had different ideas about Reconstruction. Filling in the chart below will help you understand these differences.

Policy	Abraham Lincoln	Wade-Davis Bill	Andrew Johnson	Radical Republicans
Amnesty and pardon for Confederates				
Procedure for readmitting southern states to the Union				
Rights and treatment of former slaves (freedmen)				
Formation of state governments				

Focus on U.S. History:
The Era of the Civil War and Reconstruction

Freedom's Choices

Newly freed slaves had to make choices. Would they stay on their old plantations? Would they work for wages or sharecrop? Here's how some ex-slaves described their situation.

> After the war, many soldiers came to my mistress, Mrs. Blakely, trying to make her free me. I told them I was free, but I did not want to go anywhere—that I wanted to stay in the only home that I had ever known.—Aunt Adeline

> Sometimes we would meet a white man, and he would say, "If you come work for me on my farm, when the crops are in, I give you five bushels of corn, five gallons of molasses, some ham meat, and all our clothes and vittles [food] while you work for me."—Robert Falls

> When the war was over, Master told us, "You are free now, just like I am, and as you have no places to go, you can stay on and work on halvers [for fifty percent of the crop]." We stayed on three years, after slavery. We got little money, but we got room and board and didn't have to work too hard. It was enough difference to tell you was no slaves anymore.—Lewis Bonner

> The white man says he's going to see that the sharecropper gets something to eat an' some clothes to wear, up to a specified amount. An' the cropper, he promises to work the land like the white man wants it done. An' when the crop is gathered, the sharecropper, he's gotta pay half of the corn and the cotton that he grows on the land as rent; an' he gotta pay for all the groceries, clothes, an' medicine an' doctor bills that he had while he was growing the crop.—Sarah Wilson

> In those days, the Negroes could not get out and get jobs, like they can now. If we went to another white man and asked him for a job, he asked us, "Aren't you livin' with so-an'-so?" We say, "Yes, sir." Then, he would say to us, "You will have to go to him with your trouble. He is your boss." And that was exactly what we had to do.—Rosa Pollard

Directions: With some classmates, role-play a black family discussing what they should do now that they are free. Will you stay and work for your former master/mistress? Will you move on to new land, or to a town, or even to a different state?

80   *Focus on U.S. History:*
The Era of the Civil War and Reconstruction

Reconstruction and You

Directions: People's roles in Reconstruction, and their views of it, varied depending on their personal situation and character. Imagine you are each person below. Describe your role in Reconstruction and what you think about it.

1. You are a **Radical Republican**.

2. You are a **poor white Southerner**.

3. You fought as a **soldier** in the Civil War, and you have now returned to your small southern **farm**. You have never owned slaves.

4. You own a **large cotton plantation**. Your hundred slaves are now free.

5. You are a **carpetbagger** from the North.

6. You are a **southern scalawag**.

7. You work for the **Freedmen's Bureau**.

The Reconstruction Amendments

Three amendments to the U.S. Constitution were ratified during the Reconstruction years. Here are their major provisions.

Amendment XIII

Section 1. Neither slavery nor involuntary servitude, except as a punishment for crime whereof the party shall have been duly convicted, shall exist within the United States, or any place subject to their jurisdiction.

Amendment XIV

Section 1. All persons born or naturalized in the United States, and subject to the jurisdiction thereof, are citizens of the United States and of the state wherein they reside. No State shall make or enforce any law which shall abridge the privileges or immunities of citizens of the United States; nor shall any State deprive any person of life, liberty, or property, without due process of law; nor deny to any person within its jurisdiction the equal protection of the laws.

Amendment XV

Section 1. The right of citizens of the United States to vote shall not be denied or abridged by the United States or by any State on account of race, color, or previous condition of servitude.

Directions: Answer these questions about the amendments.

Thirteenth Amendment

1. a. What is the basic provision of the Thirteenth Amendment? _____

   _____

   b. What does the Thirteenth Amendment *fail* to provide for? _____

   _____

Fourteenth Amendment

2. a. What people are U.S. citizens, according to the Fourteenth Amendment? _____

   _____

   b. What was the purpose of the statement of citizenship? _____

   _____

(continued)

The Reconstruction Amendments *(continued)*

3. a. What are the "privileges or immunities of citizens of the United States"? _____

    _____

    b. Define "due process of law." _____

    _____

    c. Define "equal protection of the laws." _____

    _____

    d. Why were these clauses included in this amendment? _____

    _____

4. Summarize the other provisions of the Fourteenth Amendment.

    Section 2: _____

    _____

    Section 3: _____

    _____

    Section 4: _____

    _____

Fifteenth Amendment

5. a. What is the basic provision of the Fifteenth Amendment? _____

    _____

    b. Why was this amendment adopted? _____

    _____

    c. List some of the ways the South was able to avoid application of this amendment.

    _____

    _____

Extra Challenge: Find examples in news reports of the "due process" and "equal protection" clauses of the Constitution being applied today.

Black Codes

After the slaves became free, southern states passed laws to keep blacks from real freedom. Here are some examples of these "black codes."

Mississippi Vagrant Act (1865)

All freedmen, free Negroes, and mulattoes over the age of eighteen years, found with no lawful employment or business, or found unlawfully assembling themselves together, either in the day or night time . . . shall be deemed vagrants, and on conviction thereof shall be fined . . . and imprisoned.

In case any freedman, free Negro or mulatto shall fail for five days after the imposition of any fine . . . to pay the same, that it shall be . . . the duty of the sheriff . . . to hire out said freedman, free Negro or mulatto, to any person who will, for the shortest period of service, pay said fine.

Louisiana Farm Labor Act (1865)

Bad work shall not be allowed. Failing to obey reasonable orders, neglect of duty, and leaving home without permission will be deemed disobedience; impudence, swearing, or indecent language to or in the presence of the employer, his family, or agent, or quarreling and fighting with one another, shall be deemed disobedience [and fined]. . . . All difficulties arising between the employers and laborers shall be settled by the former.

Florida Act on Public Places (1866)

If any Negro, mulatto, or other person of color shall intrude himself into any religious or other public assembly of white persons, or into any railroad car or other public vehicle set aside for the exclusive accommodation of white people, he shall be deemed to be guilty of a misdemeanor, and upon conviction shall be sentenced to stand in the pillory for one hour, or be whipped.

Mississippi Apprentice Law (1865)

It shall be the duty of all . . . civil officers . . . to report to the probate courts . . . all freedmen, free Negroes, and mulattoes under the age of eighteen . . . who are orphans, or whose parent or parents have not the means or who refuse to provide for and support said minors . . . the clerk of said court [will] apprentice said minors to some competent and suitable person . . . the former owner of said minors shall have the preference.

(continued)

Black Codes (continued)

Mississippi Penal Law (1865)

   Any freedman, free Negro, or mulatto committing malicious mischief . . . seditious speeches, insulting gestures, language, or acts, or assaults on any person . . . shall, upon conviction thereof . . . be fined . . . and may be imprisoned.

Directions: You are a free black person living under the provisions of the "black codes" you've just read above. Put a checkmark next to any of the things you do below that violate one of the codes. Also, note which part of what law you're violating.

_____ 1. You leave work at noon to visit your sick grandmother.

   _____

_____ 2. You get together with a group of friends for a game of dice.

   _____

_____ 3. You join a group of whites meeting to discuss crop prices.

   _____

_____ 4. A coworker hits you with her hoe, and you start yelling at her.

   _____

_____ 5. A white man driving a wagon forces you off the road, and you shake your fist at him in anger.

   _____

_____ 6. Your church isn't holding services this Sunday, so you attend the whites' Baptist church services instead.

   _____

_____ 7. You're tired and it's extremely hot, so you take a 10-minute break from work.

   _____

_____ 8. You're 16 and your parents have both died; you are running your family's small farm.

   _____

Challenge Question: Under the "black codes," why would a dispute between you and your employer almost certainly be decided in your employer's favor?

Focus on U.S. History:
The Era of the Civil War and Reconstruction

Name _____

Date _____

White Southerners and Reconstruction

Major General Carl Schurz toured the South after the war and reported his findings to President Johnson. He was most concerned about the attitudes of former supporters of the Confederacy and former slave owners. Here are parts of his 1866 report.

Treason [against the United States] does . . . not appear odious in the South. The people are not impressed with any sense of its criminality. And . . . there is, as yet, among the southern people an *utter absence of national feeling.* . . .

The principal cause of that want of national spirit which has existed in the South so long, and at last gave birth to the rebellion, was that the southern people cherished, cultivated, idolized their peculiar interests and institutions in preference to those which they had in common with the rest of the American people.

Major General
Carl Schurz

In at least nineteen cases out of twenty the reply I received to my inquiry about their views on the new system [of labor] was uniformly this: "You cannot make the Negro work without physical compulsion."

There is another popular notion prevalent in the South. . . . It is that the Negro exists for the special object of raising cotton, rice, and sugar *for the whites,* and that it is illegitimate for him to indulge, like other people, in the pursuit of his own happiness in his own way.

When the rebellion was put down they found themselves not only conquered in a political and military sense, but economically ruined. . . . From early youth they have been acquainted with but one system of labor, and with that one system they have been in the habit of identifying all their interests. They know of no way to help themselves but the one they are accustomed to. . . . To try [wage or contract labor] they consider an experiment which they cannot afford to make while their wants are urgent.

One reason the southern people are so slow in accommodating themselves to the new order of things is, that they confidently expect soon to be permitted to regulate matters according to their own notions.

Directions: Write a follow-up report by Schurz in the 1870's that tells how the Reconstruction problems he predicted because of white Southerners' attitudes and preconceptions became reality.

Focus on U.S. History:
The Era of the Civil War and Reconstruction

Name _____

Date _____

Impeachment—Yes or No?

Here are the charges brought against President Johnson in the U.S. Congress, as evidence that he should be removed from office.

Impeachment Articles, U.S. House of Representatives (1868)

That said Andrew Johnson, President of the United States . . . unmindful of the high duties of his office, of his oath of office, and of the requirement of the Constitution that he should take care that the laws be faithfully executed, did unlawfully and in violation of the Constitution and laws of the United States issue an order in writing for the removal of Edwin M. Stanton from the office of Secretary for the Department of War, said Edwin M. Stanton having been theretofore duly appointed and commissioned, by and with the advice and consent of the Senate of the United States . . . which order was unlawfully issued with intent then and there to violate the act entitled "An act regulating the tenure of certain civil offices". . . whereby said Andrew Johnson, President of the United States, did then and there commit and was guilty of a high misdemeanor in office.

Directions: Your job is to evaluate the validity of these charges against President Johnson.

• Did Johnson do what the impeachment articles charge him with?

• Was what he did a violation of the Constitution?

• Whatever Johnson did, were his actions a valid reason to impeach him and find him guilty according to the provisions of the U.S. Constitution?

Extra Challenge: Explain the impact on U.S. government if President Johnson had been found guilty and removed from office.

President Johnson

Focus on U.S. History:
The Era of the Civil War and Reconstruction

Women and the Vote

Women had been very active in *abolitionism,* the movement to end slavery. But they were not pleased with the Fourteenth and Fifteenth Amendments. Here's what Elizabeth Cady Stanton, one of the first fighters for women's rights, had to say about these amendments.

To the Editor:

Sir: by an amendment of the Constitution, ratified by three fourths of the loyal states, the black man is declared free. . . . The black man is . . . in a political point of view, far above the educated women of the country. The representative women of the nation have done their uttermost for the last thirty years to secure freedom for the Negro, and so long as he was lowest in the scale of being we were willing to press his claims; but now, as the celestial gate to civil rights is slowly moving on its hinges, it becomes a serious question whether we had better stand aside and see the black man walk into the kingdom first.

All wise women should oppose the Fifteenth Amendment for two reasons.

1st. Because it is invidious to their sex. Look at it from what point you will and in every aspect, it reflects the old idea of woman's inferiority, her subject condition. 2nd. We should oppose the measure, because men have no right to pass it without our consent. . . . If women understood this pending proposition in all its bearings . . . there would be an overwhelming vote against the admission of another man to the ruling power of this nation, until they themselves were first enfranchised. . . . [I]n tamely and silently submitting to this insult . . . it is licking the hand that forges a new chain for our degradation; it is endorsing the old idea that woman's divinely ordained position is at man's feet, and not on an even platform by his side.

It is told us in all seriousness, that the word *male* is not in the Fifteenth Amendment, as though that atoned for its infamy, and rendered it worthy of woman's support. Why should the word *male* be in it? Three times solemnly muttered in the Fourteenth, it needed no repetition in the Fifteenth.

Elizabeth Cady Stanton

Directions: From these readings, summarize the reasons why women's rights advocates were opposed to the Fourteenth and Fifteenth Amendments. Were they for equal rights for all people?

*Focus on U.S. History:
The Era of the Civil War and Reconstruction*

Black Leaders of Reconstruction

Directions: Many outstanding blacks rose to positions of leadership during Reconstruction. Match the letter of each name on the right with the correct description on the left.

_____ 1. U.S. congressman; during the Civil War, he sailed a Confederate warship out of Charleston Harbor and delivered it to Union forces.

(a) Joseph Rainey

_____ 2. Head of the Emanuel African Methodist Episcopal Church of Charleston, S.C.

(b) Robert Smalls

_____ 3. Became acting governor of Louisiana after the former governor was impeached.

(c) Robert B. Elliott

_____ 4. The second black U.S. senator, from Mississippi.

(d) Blanche K. Bruce

_____ 5. The first black U.S. congressman, he served five terms.

(e) Jefferson Long

_____ 6. Young Philadelphia woman who taught newly freed slaves of Port Royal, S.C.; granddaughter of a prominent abolitionist.

(f) John H. Rock

_____ 7. Associate justice of the South Carolina supreme court.

(g) Hiram Revels

_____ 8. U.S. congressman from South Carolina, educated at Eton in England.

(h) Robert Cardozo

_____ 9. Took over Jefferson Davis's seat in the U.S. Senate.

(i) Richard H. Cain

_____ 10. Principal of the largest black school in South Carolina.

(j) Charlotte Forten

_____ 11. First black lawyer to argue a case before the U.S. Supreme Court.

(k) P.B.S. Pinchback

_____ 12. U.S. congressman from Georgia who had to hide from violent antiblacks on election day.

(l) Jonathan Wright

Extra Challenge: Why are there so few women on this list?

Focus on U.S. History:
The Era of the Civil War and Reconstruction

The Ku Klux Klan

The Ku Klux Klan terrorized blacks in the postwar South. Here are some black people's memories of the Klan.

If you got so you made good money an' had a good farm, the Ku Klux'd come an' murder you. The gov'ment built the colored people schoolhouses, an' the Ku Klux went to work an' burn 'em down. They'd go to the jails an' take the colored men out, an' knock their brains out, an' break their necks, an' throw 'em in the river.

Men you thought was your friends was Ku Kluxes. You deal with 'em in the stores daytime, an' at night they come out to your house an' kill you.—Pierce Harper

Marster jus' laugh. He told us that we weren't goin' to be hurt, if we were good. He said that it was only the bad blacks that were goin' to be got after by the Ku Klux.—Nicey Pugh

No one knew when the Klux comin'. All a-sudden, up they gallops on horses, all covered with hoods, and burst right into the house. . . . I'd hear them comin' when they hit the lane, and I'd holler, "The Klux is comin'." It was my job, after dark, listenin' for the Klux. Then, I got under the bed.—William Hamilton

The Klux would carry the blacks to Turk Creek bridge, and make them set up on the banisters of the bridge; then, they would shoot them off the banisters into the water.—Brawley Gilmore

Directions: You are a member of a rural southern black family during the Reconstruction era of Klan terror. Discuss various strategies for keeping yourselves safe from the Klan with other family members.

Ku Klux Klan terrorizing a family at home

Focus on U.S. History:
The Era of the Civil War and Reconstruction

Slavery vs. Freedom

Directions: Study these pictures. Then, from all you have learned about Reconstruction, write an essay discussing how, and how much, life at the end of Reconstruction was different for blacks than it was in slavery.

Picking cotton

Freedmen's Bureau School in Vicksburg, Mississippi

The Compromise of 1877

Here are the votes tallied in the 1876 presidential election:

	Popular Vote	**First Electoral Vote Count**	**Second Electoral Vote Count**
Samuel J. Tilden	4,284,020	184	184
Rutherford B. Hayes	4,036,570	165	185

Directions: Answer the following questions.

1. Whom did most people vote for? _____

2. Who had the most electoral votes on the first count? _____

3. How many electoral votes were needed to win the election? _____

4. How did politicians arrive at the figures for the second electoral vote count?

_____

_____

Extra Challenge: After answering the questions above, continue by imagining you are each of the following people. What is your opinion of the Compromise of 1877? If you don't like the compromise, what alternate solution do you have for the election controversy?

---

1. You are an **African-American former slave**.

2. You are **southern political leader**.

3. You are a **northern Republican**.

*Focus on U.S. History:
The Era of the Civil War and Reconstruction*

Reconstruction Time Line

Directions: Add the Reconstruction-era events listed here to the time line you began in Units 1 and 2. Include a brief description of each event. Illustrations also enhance your time line.

Abraham Lincoln announces "Ten Percent Plan."

Wade-Davis bill is enacted.

Southern states enact "black codes."

Freedmen's Bureau is established.

Abraham Lincoln is assassinated.

Joint Committee on Reconstruction forms.

Thirteenth Amendment is ratified.

Ku Klux Klan forms.

Civil Rights Bill of 1866

Memphis race riots

First Reconstruction Act

Tenure of Office Act

Second Reconstruction Act

Andrew Johnson is impeached.

Fourth Reconstruction Act

Andrew Johnson is acquitted.

Fourteenth Amendment is ratified.

U.S. Grant is elected U.S. president.

Fifteenth Amendment is ratified.

Force Bills are enacted.

First black U.S. congressmen are seated.

Liberal Republican party nominates Greeley.

Freedmen's Bureau closes.

Grant is reelected.

Democrats win control of U.S. House of Representatives.

Civil Rights Bill of 1875

Disputed U.S. presidential election

Compromise of 1877

Last federal troops withdraw from South.

Ulysses S. Grant

Focus on U.S. History:
The Era of the Civil War and Reconstruction

ANSWERS
ADDITIONAL ACTIVITIES
ASSESSMENTS

Unit 1: The Road to War

Worksheet 1: Mapping Slave and Free States (page 7)

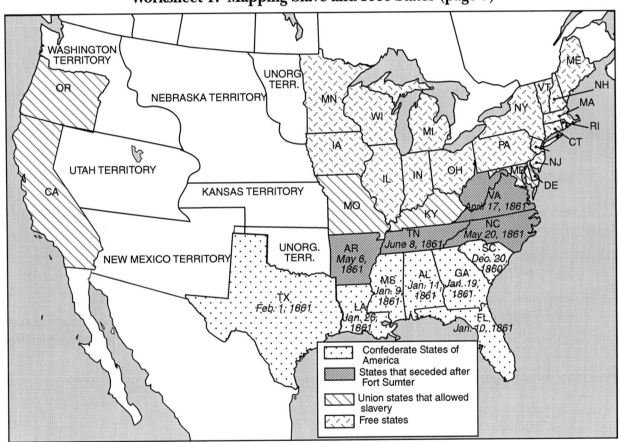

Worksheet 2: Sectional Conflicts (page 8)

Best-selling novel: 1852

Uncle Tom's Cabin is published in book form.

Becomes wildly popular, fans antislavery feelings in the North; angers the South.

Proslavery mob: 1856

Lawrence, Kansas, is sacked.

Proslavery settlers attack, sack the antislavery town.

New bill: 1854

The Kansas-Nebraska Act is passed.

Repeals the part of Missouri Compromise banning slavery north of 36°30'.

Antislavery raiders: 1859

John Brown's raid on Harpers Ferry, Virginia

Brown seizes federal arsenal, hopes slaves will join him; South is outraged; North makes Brown a hero and martyr.

Omnibus bill: 1850

Missouri Compromise

Solves the problem of slavery in the territories, temporarily.

Union loses first member: December 1860

South Carolina secedes.

Other southern states will follow suit; the Union begins to disintegrate.

Proslavery settlers killed: 1856

Pottawatomie Massacre

John Brown and six followers avenge the Lawrence attack by murdering five proslavery settlers in Kansas.

First shots: April 1861

Confederate attack on Fort Sumter

Confederate forces open fire on the federal fort in Charleston Harbor; the Civil War begins.

New political party: 1854

Republican Party is formed.

People opposed to slavery in the territories formed this party, which soon became a potent political force.

Stricter law: 1850

Passage of new Fugitive Slave Law

Provisions for strict enforcement of the law and swift, secretive return of escaped slaves on little evidence deeply anger Northerners.

Union loses five more states: January 1861

Florida, Alabama, Georgia, Louisiana, and Mississippi secede.

The breakup of the Union accelerates.

State campaign debates: 1858

Lincoln–Douglas debates

The debates call attention to the slavery debate in the North and bring Abraham Lincoln to national prominence.

Court rules: 1857

Dred Scott decision

The Supreme Court rules that slaves are not citizens and so can't sue in federal court; also, declares the Missouri Compromise unconstitutional; North is very alarmed.

New American nation: 1861

The Confederate States of America form.

Southern secession solidifies into a new nation.

Vicious violence: 1856

Congressman Brooks of South Carolina beats Senator Sumner unconscious on the floor of the U.S. Senate in retaliation for Sumner's antislavery speech.

Northerners use the attack as proof of slavery's brutalizing effects; Southerners hail Brooks as a hero.

Unacceptable candidate: 1860

Abraham Lincoln is elected U.S. president.

South Carolina, then other southern states, use Lincoln's election as an excuse to secede, since forces that supposedly hate the South have elected Lincoln.

Competing constitutions: 1856–1858

"Bleeding Kansas"

Strife is ongoing in Kansas as proslavery and antislavery forces compete for control of the territory.

Kentucky senator's compromise: 1861

The Crittendon Compromise

Senator Crittendon of Kentucky proposes a constitutional amendment that compromises on slavery in the territories; Lincoln rejects it, and the proposal dies.

Worksheet 3: Political Parties and Their Stands (page 10)

Whig party

Most members: mainly Easterners

Slavery in existing states: split on this issue

Slavery in territories: no

Popular sovereignty: no

Immigration: not a party policy

Democratic party

Most members: mixed at first, mainly Southerners by 1850's

Slavery in existing states: split at first, then proslavery as the party became mostly southern

Slavery in territories: yes

Popular sovereignty: yes

Immigration: not a particular party concern at this time

American (Know-Nothing) party

Most members: a national party (all sections)

Slavery in existing states: split (but antiblack)

Slavery in territories: not a focus

Popular sovereignty: not a focus

Immigration: anti-immigration and anti-immigrant (also anti-Catholic)

Republican party

Most members: North, East

Slavery in existing states: anti-, but not abolitionist

Slavery in territories: no

Popular sovereignty: no

Immigration: liberal policy

Challenge Questions

1. Liberty party: Was for universal emancipation achieved gradually by law.

   Free Soil party: Opposed extension of slavery into the territories.

2. Cotton Whigs: proslavery; moved to Democratic party.

   Conscience Whigs: radical Northerners, antislavery; moved to Republican party.

   Silver Gray Whigs: Northerners unopposed to slavery; moved to Democratic party.

Worksheet 4: Which Party for You? (page 11)

Likely party choices:

1. Republican
2. Free Soil
3. Democratic or Whig
4. American
5. Liberty (others duck abolition issue)
6. Democratic
7. Democratic
8. Whig/Republican

Worksheet 5: Graphing Election Results (page 12)

1.

1848

Candidate	Popular %	Electoral %
Taylor	47%	56%
Cass	43%	44%
Van Buren	10%	-

1852

Candidate	Popular %	Electoral %
Pierce	54%	86%
Scott	46%	14%

1856

Candidate	Popular %	Electoral %
Buchanan	45%	59%
Frémont	33%	38%
Fillmore	22%	3%

1860

Candidate	Popular %	Electoral %
Lincoln	40%	59%
Douglas	29%	4%
Breckinridge	18%	24%
Bell	13%	13%

2. Whig

3. Republican

4. Northern/southern, antislavery/proslavery split in the party resulted in northern Democrats nominating Douglas and southern Democrats nominating Breckinridge.

5. The antislavery Liberty party and the Democratic "Barnburners"—Democrats opposed to extension of slavery into the territories.

6. Remaining bits of the Whig and American (Know-Nothing) parties attempting to sidestep the slavery split by announcing support of the Constitution; most of its support came from border states.

Worksheet 6: North or South? (page 13)

Mistress of plantation: S

Public school: N

Coal miner: N (Pennsylvania)

Bookbinder: N (runaway slave)

Home education: S (plantation)

Work at age seven or eight: N/S (factory child/ slave)

Male head of household/honor: S

Irish immigrant: N

Machine tool factory: N

Teen girl/textile mill: N

Teen girl/ladylike: S

Whaling voyage: N

Children gone: S (slave)

Canal worker: N (possibly S)

Tobacco: S

Backcountry: S

Wheat farm: N

Farm machinery: N

Cotton fields: S

Worksheet 7: The Dred Scott Decision (page 14)

People:

Dred and Harriet Scott, black slaves; Dr. John Emerson (deceased), Dred Scott's master; Mrs. Emerson and her brother John A. Sanford (to whom Mrs. Emerson transferred ownership of Scott); Chief Justice Taney, principal Supreme Court figure in the case

Three major questions:

1. Was Dred Scott a citizen of Missouri or of the United States and thus entitled to sue in federal court?

2. Did Scott become free when he stayed in Illinois?

3. Did Scott become free when he stayed in territory declared free by the Missouri Compromise?

Taney's decisions:

1. No. Blacks had never been considered as covered by the Declaration of Independence or the U.S. Constitution, so they cannot be citizens or sue in federal court.

2. No. Once Scott was back in Missouri, Illinois laws no longer applied to him.

3. No. The Missouri Compromise was unconstitutional because it deprived slaveowners of their property (slaves) without due process.

Outcome: Slavery could not now be banned from U.S. territories.

Impact in North: Northerners were agitated; it seemed the South was trying to impose slavery everywhere.

Impact in South: Delight and satisfaction; opened way to expand slavery into the territories.

Worksheet 12: Party Platforms (page 22)

1. <u>Republican party:</u> No slavery in the territories under any circumstances.

2. <u>Democratic party (Douglas):</u> Don't disturb slavery as it now exists.

3. <u>Democratic party (Breckinridge):</u> Slavery in territories is okay.

4. Duck the issues by declaring that the Constitution rules all.

Worksheet 13: The Confederate Constitution (page 23)

1. Same three-fifths provision as U.S. Constitution.

2. U.S. Constitution provided for the end of the African slave trade by 1808.

3. In the U.S. Constitution, the term is four years, and the president is eligible for reelection.

4. Same as U.S. Constitution.

5. In the U.S. Constitution, Congress decides on laws for the territories and can exclude slavery from the territories.

6. The U.S. Constitution has no provision of this kind.

Additional Activity Suggestions

You could have students do any of the following additional activities.

1. Read *Uncle Tom's Cabin* and explain the ways in which it is and is not an accurate picture of life with slavery in the South.

2. Explain how third parties and the split in the Democratic party affected presidential election outcomes from 1848 to 1860.

3. Write a position paper applying the North's "free labor" ideology to the question of slavery in the territories.

4. Write two newspaper editorials about one of the events described in the "Sectional Conflicts" activity. One editorial will run in a northern newspaper, the other in a southern newspaper.

Assessment

1. This unit's concluding activity—"Was the War Inevitable?"—provides an excellent assessment vehicle. Alternatively, you could ask students to support or reject the following statement: The Civil War was an unavoidable result of sectional conflicts.

Unit 2: Fighting the War

Worksheet 2: Mapping the War (page 33)

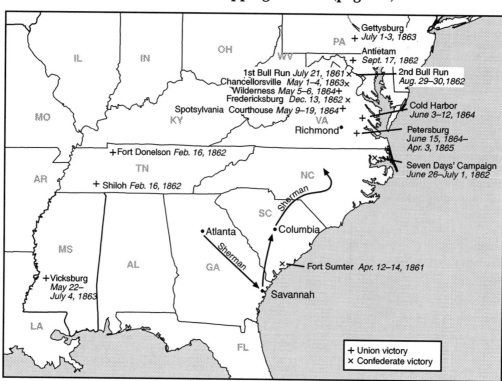

The following battle sites are labeled on the map:

- Gettysburg July 1–3, 1863 +
- Antietam Sept. 17, 1862 +
- 1st Bull Run *July 21, 1861* ×
- 2nd Bull Run *Aug. 29–30, 1862*
- Chancellorsville *May 1–4, 1863* ×
- Wilderness *May 5–6, 1864* +
- Fredericksburg *Dec. 13, 1862* ×
- Spotsylvania Courthouse *May 9–19, 1864* +
- Cold Harbor June 3–12, 1864
- Richmond •
- Petersburg June 15, 1864–Apr. 3, 1865
- Fort Donelson *Feb. 16, 1862* +
- Seven Days' Campaign June 26–July 1, 1862
- Shiloh *Feb. 16, 1862* +
- Atlanta •
- Columbia •
- Fort Sumter *Apr. 12–14, 1861* ×
- Vicksburg May 22–July 4, 1863 +
- Savannah •

+ Union victory
× Confederate victory

Worksheet 3: Strengths and Weaknesses (page 34)

1. **South.** Hard to sustain an agricultural economy in wartime; doesn't provide the matériel needed to fight a war.

2. **South.** Provides strong motivation for fighting.

3. **North.** Makes it easier to finance the northern war effort.

4. **North.** Provides efficient means to move troops and support items.

5. **South.** Gives an important tactical advantage.

6. **North.** Fresh troops, reinforcements, support items must all be brought in from away.

7. **North.** Many factories are available to produce needed wartime matériel.

8. **South.** Defensive warfare is less costly in men and matériel; leaders and men are more likely to be familiar with the terrain and climate; men are more motivated.

9. **North.** Gives the North control of the seas and the important rivers.

10. **South.** Provides strong motivation, support for war effort.

11. **South.** Impedes united war effort and leadership.

12. **South.** Makes it difficult to construct a national war effort at first.

Worksheet 4: The Call for Volunteers (page 36)

Nationalistic appeals: Irish regiment, Irish hero, glory of the other Irish regiments, the American eagle

Economic appeals: $150 bounty; state aid

Quality-of-life appeals: Will go at once into comfortable quarters and receive full rations of the best the market affords.

Worksheet 6: The Technology of War (page 38)

Hot-air balloon: Used to observe enemy movements and troop numbers, to send messages, to draw maps.

Military telegraph: Provided rapid communications among army leaders and sections.

Ironclad ship: Used little but heralded the end of the wooden warship era.

Rifles:

Bullets/cannonball measure:

Huge cannon: Much greater firepower; used in forts and on navy vessels to protect troops on land.

Navigational tools:

Railroad artillery: Gave artillery greater mobility.

Worksheet 7: The Battles (page 40)

You can assign some of the battles to individual students or small groups. (Casualty figures are approximate.)

1. <u>Fort Sumter:</u> April 12, 1861. One or two casualties for North. The war begins; the battle brings out a flood of volunteers in the North, and four more southern states secede.

2. <u>First Battle of Bull Run (First Manassas):</u> July 21, 1861. North 3,000; South 2,000. First major battle of the war: South shocks North; romantic view of the war is shaken; southern morale soars; North starts to realize it will be hard to put down the secession.

3. <u>Fort Donelson:</u> February 12–16, 1862. Grant leads first major win for the North, rises to attention.

4. <u>La Glorieta Pass:</u> March 28, 1862. Union forces and Texas army clash indecisively beyond Santa Fe; Union forces destroy Texas supply train and end Confederate threat to the Far West.

5. <u>Shiloh:</u> April 6–7, 1862. North 10,000; South 10,000. Confederates crush Union troops and then fall back; both sides shaken by losses; ends all romantic notions of the war.

6. <u>Seven Days' Campaign:</u> June 25–July 1, 1862. North 16,000; South 20,000. Lee's troops force Union forces back from near Richmond; northern morale plummets.

7. <u>Second Battle of Bull Run (Second Manassas):</u> August 29–30, 1862. Lee beats Union soundly again, regains momentum.

8. <u>Antietam (Sharpsburg):</u> September 17, 1862. North 12,400; South 10,700. McClellan's army stops Lee's from invading the North and inflicts heavy losses, but McClellan fails to press forward to victory; northern "victory" gives Lincoln opportunity to issue Emancipation Proclamation.

9. <u>Fredericksburg:</u> December 13, 1862. North 12,600; South about 5,000. Union general Burnside suffers terrible defeat; northern morale hit hard.

10. <u>Stones River (Murfreesboro):</u> December 31, 1862–January 2, 1863. North 12,900; South 11,700. Union wins narrowly; loss of men hits South hard.

11. <u>Chancellorsville:</u> May 1–5, 1863; North 17,000; South 12,000. South wins but suffers heavy casualties and loses Stonewall Jackson; Union morale dealt another big blow.

12. <u>Gettysburg:</u> July 1–3, 1863. North 23,045; South 20,451. Turning point of the war—Lee fails to win on northern soil, loses momentum of victory.

13. <u>Vicksburg:</u> May 18–July 4, 1863. Siege successful; Union now controls Mississippi River.

14. <u>Chickamauga:</u> September 19–20, 1863. North 16,000; South 18,000. Confederates win but gain little and have heavy casualties.

15. <u>Chattanooga:</u> ends November 23–25, 1863. North about 6,000; South about 7,000. North halts string of Confederate advances, clears way for invasion of Georgia.

16. <u>Wilderness:</u> May 5–7, 1864. North 18,000; South 8,000. Grant holds fast against Lee in spite of heavy losses; gives a big, much needed boost to northern morale.

17. <u>Spotsylvania Court House:</u> May 8–19, 1864. North 17,000; South 8,000. Series of fierce fights results in high casualties on both sides, losses the South can't afford.

18. <u>Cold Harbor:</u> June 3–12, 1864. North 7,000; South 1,500. Another Grant-Lee fight, which the Confederates win; Union suffers its 7,000 casualties in 20 minutes; northern public opinion very unfavorable.

19. <u>Fall of Atlanta and Sherman's march:</u> September 2, 1864, and November–December, 1864. Atlanta's fall rallies pro-Lincoln forces in the North and staggers the South; the destructive march crushes southern spirit and destroys southern resources.

20. <u>Fall of Richmond and Petersburg:</u> April 3, 1865. Lee realizes it is futile to continue fighting; he surrenders April 9, 1865, at Appomattox Court House.

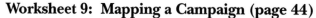

Worksheet 9: Mapping a Campaign (page 44)

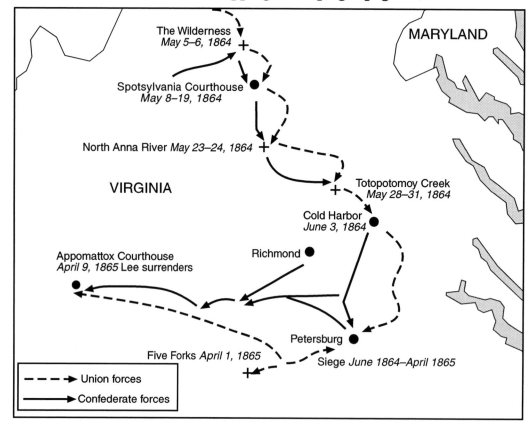

Worksheet 11: The Emancipation Proclamation (page 47)

1. Emancipation: act of freeing from bondage

   Proclamation: an official, formal public announcement

2. It did not free slaves in slave-holding Union states or in areas of Confederate states already controlled by the federal government.

3. It would be enforced by the U.S. military.

4. Emancipation was not a popular war aim in the North in the early years of the war and was opposed by the border states within the Union. By the fall of 1862, Lincoln felt he needed to announce emancipation to weaken the South and to stave off possible recognition of the Confederate States of America by European nations.

5. They were outraged and viewed it as a blatant incitement to the slaves to rebel.

6. Some thought it didn't go far enough. It also inflamed antiblack feelings in the North, fanning fears of a wholesale black migration from the South. Most blacks saw it as a beacon of change to come.

Worksheet 12: Graphing the War (page 48)

<u>Population bar graph:</u> shows enormous numerical advantage North had over the South in terms of potential troop strength and workers.

<u>Line graph:</u> North had many more men and increased this advantage proportionally as the war went on. You'd expect this to be true, given the population contrast in the bar graph.

Worksheet 13: Time Line of the War (page 49)

Fort Sumter supply ship turns back. February 1861

Lincoln's first inaugural. March 1861

West Virginia is formed. June 1861

Union blockade of the South begins. July 1861

The *Trent* affair. November 1861

Confederate draft law. April 1862

Slavery in Washington, D.C, is abolished. April 1862

Slavery is outlawed in the territories. June 1862

Lee takes command of Army of Northern Virginia. June 1862

Preliminary Emancipation Proclamation. September 1862

Emancipation Proclamation goes into effect. January 1863

Union draft law. March 1863

Bureau of Colored Troops is established. May 1863

New York City draft riots. July 1863

Gettysburg Address. November 1863

Grant takes command of all Union armies. March 1864

Lincoln is reelected. November 1864

U.S. Congress approves Thirteenth Amendment. January 1865

Lincoln's second inaugural. March 1865

Lee surrenders at Appomattox Court House. April 9, 1865

Lincoln is assassinated. April 14, 1865

Andrew Johnson becomes U.S. president. April 15, 1865

Booth is shot and killed. April 26, 1865

Union soldiers are sent home. May 1865

Thirteenth Amendment is ratified. December 1865

Additional Activity Suggestions

You could have students do any of the following additional activities.

1. Role-play a discussion among President Lincoln and his advisers about issuing the Emancipation Proclamation. What would be the advantages of announcing emancipation? What would be some drawbacks and possible dangers?

2. Create a class display of Civil War photographs showing the many different aspects of the conflict and the roles played by different people in the war.

3. View at least one video in the wonderful Ken Burns series, *The Civil War.* Or gain a deeper understanding of a crucial battle in the war by viewing the gripping *Gettysburg.*

4. If possible, visit a Civil War battle site. Share photos and park service brochures and other information about the battle site with classmates. Add some personal descriptions of the battle written by soldiers in diaries, letters, or memoirs.

5. Find the story behind any Civil War monuments or other memorials in your local area. If the war was fought in your local area, tell the story of local wartime events.

6. Report on the role played by Native Americans in the Civil War and on the effect of the war on various Native American groups.

7. Brainstorm and list all the advantages of fighting on home ground and fighting to defend your home ground.

Assessment

1. Discuss how military, political, and diplomatic leadership affected the course and outcome of the Civil War.

2. Describe the specific reasons why the Civil War can be accurately described as the "first modern war."

Unit 3: The Personal Face of War

Worksheet 1: Civil War Songs (page 57)

1. "We Are Coming"—Union

   "The Bonnie Blue Flag"—Confederate

2. "We Are Coming" was inspired by President Lincoln's call for 300,000 more soldiers to enlist in the Union army.

3. This refers to the individual southern states' rights.

4. Many Southerners earned and kept their land with their own "honest toil," but others used the toil of black slaves rather than their own toil to work their land.

Worksheet 4: Northern Women in Wartime (page 61)

First photo: Clara Barton, called the "Angel of the Battlefield." She began emergency care for wounded soldiers on the battlefield, later founded the American Red Cross.

Second photo: Dorothea Dix, an important crusader for better care for the mentally ill. During the Civil War, she supervised nurses caring for the wounded.

Bottom photo: Elizabeth Blackwell, the first female American doctor of medicine, helped organize the U.S. Sanitary Commission, for women, which worked to improve sanitary conditions at army camps and raised money for medical supplies and also enlisted volunteer women to provide supplies.

You could also ask students to identify the contributions of other women in care of soldiers during the war, such as Sally Tompkins and Kate Cumming in the South. You could assign individual reports on any of these women or a consolidated report on all.

Worksheet 7: Wartime Destruction (page 64)

The top photo shows the southern U.S. city of Richmond, Virginia, after its Civil War devastation.

The bottom photo shows the city of Sarajevo in the former Yugoslavia during that nation's recent civil war.

After the discussion about when each photograph may have been taken and what each one may show, lead a further discussion about the definition of civil war and what its effects are on the military and civilian populations, using specific historical examples to illustrate the points. Conclude by comparing the U.S. Civil War with the civil war in the former Yugoslavia, including the ways in which civilian populations and towns/cities were impacted.

Worksheet 8: Black Soldiers—Yes or No? (page 65)

1. Kentucky was a border state—slavery existed there, but the state stayed with the Union.

2. Cox: Northern Democrat

   Stevens: Republican

3. Unfair to black slaves; they have no reason to fight for a Union based on a constitution that permits slavery; white soldiers won't want to continue serving in an army that also allows black soldiers; Confederacy will treat black soldier prisoners of war as criminals and escaped slaves rather than as war prisoners under international law.

4. Union needs more soldiers, and blacks are a source; blacks can share with whites risk of death in the war; white soldiers couldn't object to that; nations throughout history have used black slaves in wartime for defensive purposes; maybe the end result of adding black troop strength to the Union army will be victory in the war and, therefore, the end of slavery.

5. Stevens's real reason for having black soldiers was to hasten the end of the war and of slavery; he spoke of these other reasons to try to gain support in Congress from those who were leery of taking steps toward equality of blacks.

Additional Activity Suggestions

You could have students do any of the following additional activities.

1. View the video *Glory* to gain a better understanding of the role and experiences of African-American soldiers in the Civil War.

2. List the number of ways in which an adult male could avoid military service during the Civil War, even after both the Union and the Confederacy passed draft laws.

3. Play or perform other Civil War songs for the class. Compare the spirit and lyrics of "Dixie" with those of "The Battle Hymn of the Republic."

4. Role-play a debate in the U.S. Congress between Peace Democrats and Republicans.

5. Write an eyewitness account of the New York City draft riots.

Assessment

1. Compare the changes in black women's and white women's lives during the Civil War.

2. Discuss the human and material costs of the war, North and South.

Unit 4: *Reconstruction*

Worksheet 1: The South, Before and After (page 78)

Family life
  Prewar: White families tended to have husbands and wives operating in their separate spheres; black slaves formed strong family bonds but were often separated involuntarily.
  Postwar: Many white women became heads of household, had to become breadwinners or farm operators; families shattered by war casualties; families displaced; black families became stronger because family members were no longer sold away and also became more like white families, with the husband the breadwinner and the wife working as a housewife.

Farms and plantations
  Prewar: Mostly prosperous in the South's strong agricultural economy.
  Postwar: Burned out in many areas, fields gone to weeds, and houses damaged, destroyed, and plundered; livestock and farm tools gone or destroyed.

Farm workers/labor force:
  Prewar: Enormous pool of slave farm workers.
  Postwar: Slave labor is gone, but many blacks remain; sharecropping system develops.

Credit and money supply
  Prewar: Both widely available in prosperous agricultural economy.
  Postwar: Confederate money is worthless; planters can't get credit to buy seeds and new farm tools; a barter system develops.

Commerce
  Prewar: Smoothly functioning agricultural economy.
  Postwar: Commerce generally destroyed; barter system develops.

Housing
  Prewar: Adequate housing stock.
  Postwar: Many buildings (rural, town, and city) destroyed or badly damaged and plundered in war.

Infrastructure
  Prewar: Adequate system.
  Postwar: Many roads, bridges, railroads, levees destroyed.

Worksheet 2: Plans for Reconstruction (page 79)

Amnesty and pardon for Confederates

  Lincoln: Pardon for all (except a very few) who take oath of loyalty.

  Wade–Davis: Confederates must swear past and present loyalty to Union.

  Johnson: Pardoned almost all, but excluded more than Lincoln.

  Radical Republicans: Former Confederate officials and army officers can't vote.

Procedure for readmitting

  Lincoln: 10% Plan—10% of a state's voting population takes oath of allegiance to Union and agrees to end slavery.

Wade–Davis: Majority of a state's voting population takes oath of allegiance and agrees to end slavery.

Johnson: Similar to Lincoln's 10% Plan; easy terms.

Radical Republicans: States must hold constitutional conventions, ratify the Fourteenth Amendment, and guarantee blacks' right to vote.

Rights and treatment of former slaves

Lincoln: No provisions for this, but did prohibit slavery.

Wade–Davis: State governments must outlaw slavery.

Johnson: Leaves this up to states; encourages states to permit blacks to vote; no slavery.

Radical Republicans: Federal government ensures that states guarantee black voting rights; Fourteenth and Fifteenth Amendments further guarantee black rights.

Formation of state governments

Lincoln: Federal government oversees formation of new state governments in states occupied by Union troops; at war's end, former Confederate states could form new governments under Lincoln's 10% plan.

Wade–Davis: States to form completely new governments after the majority vote for readmittance.

Johnson: Appoints provisional governor, who oversees formation of a new state government.

Radical Republicans: southern states under military rule; states must set up new governments via constitutional conventions.

Worksheet 5: The Reconstruction Amendments (page 82)

Thirteenth Amendment

1. a. It bans slavery.

    b. It doesn't provide for blacks' political rights.

Fourteenth Amendment

2. a. All people born or naturalized (made citizens) in the United States.

    b. To include blacks.

3. a. The rights and protections guaranteed to U.S. citizens by the U.S. Constitution.

    b. Done in accordance with the law and the Constitution.

    c. Every citizen is treated equally under the law.

    d. To protect blacks from abuses and unequal treatment by their state governments.

4. Section 2—if any state denied the vote to any part of its adult male population, its representation in Congress would be cut accordingly; this was an attempt to get states to allow blacks to vote.

    Section 3—former federal officials who had worked for the Confederacy were not allowed to hold state or federal office unless Congress voted otherwise by a two-thirds majority.

    Section 4—Confederate debt is declared void.

Fifteenth Amendment

5. a. It guarantees blacks the right to vote in every state.

    b. Many people felt strongly that blacks should have the right to vote in every state; Republicans also hoped to secure the strategic black vote for their party.

    c. Poll tax, literacy tests, terrorism, intimidation, inaccessible polling places, etc.

Worksheet 6: Black Codes (page 84)

1. Violates Louisiana Farm Labor Act provision "leaving home without permission" if you don't have your employer's permission to go.

2. Could violate Mississippi Vagrant Act by being "found unlawfully assembling."

3. Could violate Florida Act on Public Places provision that no black person "shall intrude himself into any . . . public assembly of white persons."

4. Violates Louisiana Farm Labor Act provision that black farm workers must not take part in any "quarreling and fighting with one another."

5. Violates Mississippi Penal Law barring blacks from "insulting gestures, language, or acts."

6. Violates Florida Act on Public Places provision that no black person "shall intrude himself into any religious . . . assembly of white persons."

7. Could be a violation of the Louisiana Farm Labor Act provision barring "neglect of duty."

8. Violates Mississippi Apprentice Law providing that all black orphans under the age of eighteen must be apprenticed out by the probate court.

Challenge Question: The employer makes the decision in case of disputes, and a black worker's appeal of this decision would be decided by other whites, who would almost certainly support the employer.

Worksheet 10: Black Leaders of Reconstruction (page 89)

1. b	7. l
2. i	8. c
3. k	9. g
4. d	10. h
5. a	11. f
6. j	12. e

Worksheet 13: The Compromise of 1877 (page 92)

1. Tilden

2. Tilden

3. 185

4. Democrats supported Republican Hayes in return for Republican agreement to remove the remaining federal troops from the South and let the southern states run their own affairs—i.e., in return for an end to Reconstruction.

Worksheet 14: Reconstruction Time Line (page 93)

Students can add other events in U.S. history during the Reconstruction era to this time line.

Abraham Lincoln announces "Ten Percent Plan." December 1863

Wade–Davis bill enacted. July 1864

Southern states enact "black codes." 1865–66

Freedmen's Bureau established. March 1865

Abraham Lincoln assassinated. April 1865

Joint Committee on Reconstruction forms. December 1865

Thirteenth Amendment ratified. December 1865

Ku Klux Klan forms. 1866

Civil Rights Bill of 1866. April 1866

Memphis race riots. May 1866

First Reconstruction Act. March 1867

Tenure of Office Act. March 1867

Second Reconstruction Act. July 1867

Andrew Johnson impeached. February 1868

Fourth Reconstruction Act. March 1868

Andrew Johnson acquitted. May 1868

Fourteenth Amendment ratified. July 1868

Ulysses S. Grant elected U.S. president. November 1868

Fifteenth Amendment ratified. March 1870

Force Bills enacted. 1870–1875

First black U.S. congressmen seated. December 1870

Liberal Republican party nominates Greeley. May 1872

Freedmen's Bureau closed. July 1872

Grant reelected. November 1872

Democrats win control of U.S. House of Representatives. November 1874

Civil Rights Act of 1875. March 1875

Disputed U.S. presidential election. November 1876

Compromise of 1877. January 1877

Last federal troops withdraw from South. April 1877

Additional Activity Suggestions

You could have students do any of the following additional activities.

1. Create a classroom display of political cartoons commenting on the widespread postwar corruption in state and national government. Write a brief commentary to explain each cartoon in its historical context and to support or refute its accuracy.

2. Report on the political, social, and economic position of African-Americans in the North in the post-Civil War era.

3. With classmates, do a choral reading of Walt Whitman's poem about Abraham Lincoln, "O Captain! My Captain!" (included in *Leaves of Grass*).

4. Read the chapter in John F. Kennedy's *Profiles in Courage* about Edmund G. Ross, the senator who cast the deciding vote against President Johnson's conviction at his impeachment trial.

5. Write an essay discussing the effect on American government if President Johnson had been convicted and removed from office.

6. In chart form, show the successes and failures of the Freedmen's Bureau.

Assessment

1. Analyze the successes and failures of Reconstruction as it affected African-Americans in the South. What goals—economic, social, political—were blacks able to achieve during Reconstruction? What goals remained unreached or only partially realized?

2. Discuss the reasons why Reconstruction failed. Did it go far enough? Should it have gone farther?

ADDITIONAL RESOURCES

Historical Fiction for Students

Beatty, Patricia. *Jayhawker* (Kansas, Missouri, and escaping slaves)

Burchard, Peter. *Bimby* (young slave)

_____. *The Deserter* (Civil War spy story)

_____. *Jed: The Story of a Yankee Soldier and a Southern Boy*

_____. *North by Night* (Union prisoners of war attempt to escape North)

Crane, Stephen. *The Red Badge of Courage* (young Union soldier)

Cummings, Betty Sue. *Hew Against the Grain* (Civil War deaths in a girl's family)

Fast, Howard. *Freedom Road* (freed blacks in Reconstruction)

Freedman, Florence. *Two Tickets to Freedom* (Reconstruction life)

Gauch, Patricia. *Thunder at Gettysburg*

Hansen, Joyce. *Out from This Place* (freed blacks in Reconstruction)

_____. *Which Way Freedom?* (freed blacks in Reconstruction)

Hunt, Irene. *Across Five Aprils* (conflicts in a border state family)

Hurmence, Belinda. *Tancy* (search for relatives after emancipation)

Keith, Harold. *Rifles for Watie* (the war in Kansas, and among the Cherokee)

Monjo, F.N. *Gettysburg: Tad Lincoln's Story*

_____. *Me and Willie and Pa* (Tad Lincoln)

_____. *The Vicksburg Veteran* (General Grant's son and the siege)

O'Dell, Scott. *The 290* (Confederate warship)

Perez, N.A. *The Slopes of War* (Gettysburg)

Reeder, Carolyn. *Shades of Gray* (the pacifist position)

Rinaldi, Ann. *The Last Silk Dress* (young teen's confused loyalties)

Sebestyen, Ouida. *Words by Heart* (black family in Reconstruction)

Shaara, Michael. *The Killer Angels* (battle of Gettysburg)

Wisler, Clifton. *Thunder on the Tennessee* (16-year-old southern soldier)

Nonfiction for Students

Hamilton, Virginia. *Many Thousand Gone: African Americans from Slavery to Freedom*

Hansen, Joyce. *Between Two Fires: Black Soldiers in the Civil War*

Mellon, James, ed. *Bullwhip Days: The Slaves Remember—An Oral History*

Meltzer, Milton, ed. *The Black Americans: A History in Their Own Words*

Sourcebooks on the Civil War: American Albums from the Collections of the Library of Congress (Millbrook Press): *Prelude to War, The First Battles, 1863: The Crucial Year, The Road to Appomattox, Behind the Lines, One Nation Again*

Collections of Primary Source Documents: Print

The Annals of America. Chicago: Encyclopedia Britannica, 1968.

Commager, Henry Steele, ed. *Documents of American History,* 9th ed. (2 vols.) Englewood Cliffs, NJ: Prentice-Hall, 1973.

Craven, Avery, Walter Johnson, and F. Roger Dunn. *A Documentary History of the American People.* Boston: Ginn and Company, 1951.

Hart, Albert Bushnell. *American History as Told by Contemporaries, Vol. IV: Welding of the Nation 1845–1900.* New York: The Macmillan Company, 1901.

Miller, Marion Mills, ed. *Great Debates in American History.* New York: Current Literature Publishing Company, 1913 (14 volumes in all).

Time-Life Collector's Library of the Civil War (reprints of Civil War memoirs, many volumes)

CD-ROM

America Adventure. Knowledge Adventure (also available as a DOS floppy disk).

American Journey—History in Your Hands. Research Publications.
The African-American Experience
The Civil War
Women in America

CD Sourcebook of American History. InfoBases.

Landmark Documents in American History. Facts on File (dwarfs the print collections).

World Wide Web/Internet

Sites with numerous links to U.S. history sources:

Government/Social Studies Sources (includes listings of Library of Congress exhibits, historical documents from Project Gutenburg, other social studies Web sites):
http://www.nwoca.ohio.gov/www/gov.html

History/Social Studies Web Site for K–12 Teachers (includes site map, What's New Archive, sources arranged by category):
http://www.execpc.com/~dboals/boals.html

Library of Congress home page (includes American Memory historical collections):
http://lcweb.loc.gov

Kathy Schrock's site (a Cape Cod teacher's excellent list of resources):
http://www.capecod.net/schrockguide

Civil War sites:

American Civil War: Resources on the Internet (Dakota State University):
http://www.dsu.edu:80/~jankej/civilwar.html

The American Civil War Homepage:
http://funnelweb.utcc.utk.edu/~hoemann/cwarhp.html

Library of Congress Civil War Photographs:
http://lcweb2.loc.gov/ammem/cwphome.html

The United States Civil War Center (Louisiana State University):
http://www.cwc.lsu.edu/index.htm

United States Historic Documents (primary documents in full text):
http://www.ukans.edu/carrie/docs/amdocs_index.html

Video

The Civil War (Ken Burns's 9-video PBS series)

Gettysburg

Glory

Lincoln, PBS Home Video (4-video series)

The Massachusetts 54th Colored Infantry, PBS Video

GLOSSARY

abolition—putting an end to something, wiping it out; the abolition movement, or abolitionism, wanted to end (abolish) slavery in the United States.

amnesty—a general pardon to a large group, usually issued by a government.

carpetbagger—Northerner who went South to work for Reconstruction.

desert—to leave the army without permission, with no intention of returning.

emancipation—act of freeing from bondage.

impeach—to charge a federal official with misconduct.

popular sovereignty—allowing the voters in each territory to decide for or against slavery there themselves.

proclamation—an official, formal public announcement.

Reconstruction—period of rebuilding in the South from 1865 to 1877.

scalawag—Southerner who cooperated with Reconstruction.

secede—to withdraw formally from an organization or alliance; secession is the act of seceding.

sharecropping—system of farming whereby a worker farms another person's land in return for a share of the crop.

writ of habeas corpus—legal order to bring an arrested person before a judge; this protects people from being held in jail without a trial or hearing.

Notes

Notes

Share Your Bright Ideas with Us!

We want to hear from you! Your valuable comments and suggestions will help us meet your current and future classroom needs.

Your name_____Date_____

School name_____Phone_____

School address_____

Grade level taught_____Subject area(s) taught_____Average class size_____

Where did you purchase this publication?_____

Was your salesperson knowledgeable about this product?   Yes_____   No_____

What monies were used to purchase this product?

____School supplemental budget   ____Federal/state funding   ____Personal

Please "grade" this Walch publication according to the following criteria:

Quality of service you received when purchasing ....A   B   C   D   F
Ease of use...A   B   C   D   F
Quality of content..A   B   C   D   F
Page layout ....A   B   C   D   F
Organization of material ....A   B   C   D   F
Suitability for grade level ....A   B   C   D   F
Instructional value..A   B   C   D   F

COMMENTS:_____

_____

What specific supplemental materials would help you meet your current—or future—instructional needs?

_____

Have you used other Walch publications? If so, which ones?_____

May we use your comments in upcoming communications?   ____Yes   ____No

Please **FAX** this completed form to **207-772-3105**, or mail it to:

Product Development, J. Weston Walch, Publisher, P.O. Box 658, Portland, ME 04104-0658

We will send you a **FREE GIFT** as our way of thanking you for your feedback.   **THANK YOU!**